Ken Lee
Robert Farnsworth

Introduction to

Sustainable Horticulture Science

Kendall Hunt
publishing company

Cover images © Shutterstock.com

www.kendallhunt.com
Send all inquiries to:
4050 Westmark Drive
Dubuque, IA 52004-1840

Published in the United States of America

CONTENTS

Prologue   **What Is Sustainable Horticulture?**   *1*

Fundamentals of Horticulture

CHAPTER 1   **Plant Classification and Botanical Nomenclature**   **17**

CHAPTER 2   **Plant Morphology**   **31**

CHAPTER 3   **Germination and Plant Life Cycle**   **41**

CHAPTER 4   **Plant Physiology**   **53**

CHAPTER 5   **Pollination**   **67**

CHAPTER 6   **Propagation**   **77**

CHAPTER 7   **Genetically Modified Organism**   **91**

Sustainable Horticulture

CHAPTER 8   **Soil and Compost**   **103**

CHAPTER 9   **Fertilizer**   **121**

CHAPTER 10   **Pest and Disease**   **137**

CHAPTER 11   **Plant Communities—Native, Exotic, Invasive**   **157**

CHAPTER 12   **Container Plants and Succulents**   **167**

CHAPTER 13   **Vegetable and Fruit**   **177**

CHAPTER 14   **Plants and Water**   **197**

CHAPTER 15   **Pruning**   **209**

CHAPTER 16   **Trends in Sustainable Horticulture—Urban Farming**   **221**

CHAPTER 17   **Sustainable Landscape Design—Wellness Garden**   **231**

WHAT IS SUSTAINABLE HORTICULTURE?

Relevant Words

Agriculture, Botany, Civilization, Horticulture, *Hortus Cultura*, Ornamental, Sustainable, United States Department of Agriculture (USDA)

Lab Objective

To learn about the meaning of being sustainable by identifying the difference between "*sustainable*" horticulture and "*ornamental*" horticulture.

Lab Assignment

- Visit a local nursery to identify its operations for "*practices of sustainability*" and narrate the findings with a personal assessment.
- Identify and narrate the traditional ornamental horticulture examples from your home, neighbors, or local community.
- Describe how "*ornamental*" horticulture application can be transformed into "*sustainable*" horticulture.

Lecture Outlines

© SofiaV/Shutterstock.com

What Is Horticulture?

Horticulture is the science and art of growing plants (fruits, vegetables, flowers, and any other cultivar). It also includes plant conservation, landscape restoration, soil management, landscape and garden design, construction and maintenance, and arboriculture. In contrast to agriculture, horticulture does not include large-scale crop production or animal husbandry.

WHAT IS SUSTAINABLE HORTICULTURE?

Lecture Outlines (*continued*)

What is Horticulture? (*continued*)

> *United States Department of Agriculture (USDA) definition of special crop*
> https://nifa.usda.gov/sites/default/files/resources/definition_of_specialty_crops.pdf
>
> *Horticulture is defined as that branch of agriculture concerned with growing plants that are used by people for food, for medicinal purposes, and for aesthetic gratification. Horticulture is divided into specializations. The terms used to describe these specializations derive from millennia of common usage and are sometimes at odds with botanical nomenclature. For example, vegetables are described as herbaceous plants of which some portion is eaten raw or cooked during the main part of a meal. Fruits, for horticultural purposes, are described as plants from which a more or less succulent fruit or closely related botanical structure is commonly eaten as a dessert or snack. By these definitions, plants such as tomato, squash and cucumber are considered vegetables despite the fact that the edible portion is defined botanically as a fruit. The delineation of plants by common usage was legally established in 1893 by the unanimous U.S. Supreme Court decision in the case of Nix vs. Hedden.*

Horticulturists apply their knowledge, skills, and technologies to grow intensively produced plants for human food and nonfood uses and for personal or social needs. Their work involves plant propagation and cultivation with the aim of improving plant growth, yields, quality, nutritional value, and resistance to insects, diseases, and environmental stresses. They work as gardeners, growers, therapists, designers, and technical advisors in the food and nonfood sectors of horticulture. Horticulture even refers to the growing of plants in a field or garden.

- Horticulture—*Hortus* (garden) + *Cultura* (culture)
- Art and science of growing plants—Trees, shrubs, flowers, vegetables, fruits, herbs, and nuts
- Horticulture and agriculture—Common practices (watering, weeding, fertilizing, pest control, etc.)
- Horticulture as scientific practice, such as grafting, propagation, and pruning

WHAT IS SUSTAINABLE HORTICULTURE?

Lecture Outlines (*continued*)

© Macrovector/Shutterstock. com

Division of Horticulture

- Fruit growing (pomology)—Grape growing (viticulture)
- Market gardening (vegetables and herbs)—Nut cultivation for oil production
- Ornamental cultivation (flowers, shrubs, and trees)—Floriculture, landscape horticulture, arboriculture

What Is Sustainability? (*from Wikipedia 2018. Reference purpose only*)

© Cienpies/Shutterstock.com

Sustainability (from *sustain* and *ability*) is the property of biological systems to remain diverse and productive indefinitely. Long-lived and healthy wetlands and forests are examples of sustainable biological systems. In more general terms, sustainability is the endurance of systems and processes. The organizing principle for sustainability is sustainable development, which includes the four interconnected domains: ecology, economics, politics, and culture. Sustainability Science is the study of sustainable development and environmental science.

Sustainability can also be defined as a socioecological process characterized by the pursuit of a common ideal. An ideal is, by definition, unattainable in a given time and space. However, by persistently and dynamically approaching it, the process results in a sustainable system. Healthy ecosystems and environments are necessary to the survival of humans and other organisms. Ways of reducing negative human impact are environmentally friendly chemical engineering, environmental resources management, and environmental protection. Information is gained from green computing, green chemistry, earth science, environmental science, and conservation biology. Ecological economics studies the fields of academic research that aim to address human economies and natural ecosystems.

Sustainability defined by United States Environmental Protection Agency (US EPA) https://www.epa.gov/sustainability/learn-about-sustainability#what

The National Environmental Policy Act of 1969 committed the United States to sustainability, declaring it a national policy "to create and maintain conditions under which humans and nature can exist in productive harmony, that permit fulfilling the social, economic and other requirements of present and future generations."

WHAT IS SUSTAINABLE HORTICULTURE?

Lecture Contents

What Is Sustainability? (continued)

In the years since NEPA was enacted, the public's interest in sustainability has broadened. According to the National Research Council, there are many additional drivers for sustainability. In the areas where the US has seen considerable progress in sustainability, a common driver for sustainability efforts is citizens and other stakeholders concern. In addition, sustainability practitioners are becoming more ambitious in their sustainability efforts and are working together to share best practices to ensure the greatest environmental, economic and social impact.

Source: Ken Lee

Introduction to Sustainable Horticulture

Sustainable agriculture is farming in sustainable ways based on an understanding of ecosystem services, the study of relationships between organisms and their environment. It has been defined as "an integrated system of plant and animal production practices having a site-specific application that will last over the long term."

Sustainable horticulture is the plants science, the study of relationships between organisms and their environment. It has been defined as "an integrated system of plant and animal production practices having a site-specific application that will last over the long term."

When we decided to write a text about horticulture, of course we would agree to start with an explanation of what horticulture is, and why it is important for us to consider daily. We would begin with a brief discussion on the enormous benefit of plants.

Without plants, we humans wouldn't be here. Plain and simple. Plants provide us with food, fuel, medicine, and oxygen to breathe. We build our homes with products from their limbs. Plants clean air, protect soil, and provide habitat. When plants are finished, their nutrients are recycled back into the natural system. It is a beautiful system.

The word horticulture has roots in the Latin words *hortus* and *cultura*, meaning "*garden cultivation.*" The science dates back thousands of years, and has had a profound effect on the development and lives of humans. As it is about garden cultivation, horticulture is indeed about plants. But so are the sciences of botany and agriculture. What's the difference?

Agriculture is the science of animal husbandry, and growing grains such as wheat, rye, and oats. Corn (maize) is often included as a grain, especially if it is raised for feeding animals, or as a product ingredient such as corn syrup. Botany is a thorough study of

WHAT IS SUSTAINABLE HORTICULTURE?

Lecture Contents *(continued)*

Introduction to Sustainable Horticulture *(continued)*

plants at the cellular level. A horticulturalist might be able to identify a plant by its scent. A botanist can tell you how that scent is produced.

Horticulture is the science of garden cultivation. It includes the production of fruits, nuts, vegetables, herbs, grapes, ornamental plants, medicinal plants, and a few special categories (such as Christmas tree farms). It covers just about all plants grown for science, dining, pleasure, and therapy.

How Horticulture Helped Shaping Civilization

© Cienpies/Shutterstock.com

Early humans had survived by gathering edible roots, leaves, and fruits for their food, and through hunting fish and other wild animals. They moved from place to place through the seasons, in their endless search. Some of those early humans experimented with seed collection, and around 7,000 BCE, started growing their own food. They grew their food in one of the most highly productive soils on the planet, in a region that would become known through history as the Fertile Crescent, and the "*Cradle of Civilization.*"

The land was especially fertile there due to a confluence of rivers; in this case, the confluence of the Euphrates, Tigris, and Nile rivers, in the region of the Persian Gulf (through modern-day southern Iraq, Syria, Lebanon, Jordan, Israel, and northern Egypt). A confluence of rivers is where two or more rivers meet. The land can be highly productive, because floods cause minerals, nutrients, decayed fish, and organic matter from one watershed to blend with sediment from another. Water for plants was plentiful. Gravel, sand, silt, and clay were blended perfectly for optimal drainage and fertility. Crops were grown, and all was well. People were satisfied with this scenario for several thousand more years.

Naturally, as population increased, pressure on food production increased. In 4,000 BCE, humans discovered the plow. This made planting the seeds easier, but growing at the river's edge was difficult. Ravaged by regular flooding, the struggles and movement of people continued. In 3,500 BCE, someone thought irrigation would be a good idea. "*Bring the water to an area where we are free from flooding,*" they may have exclaimed. Suddenly the idea of a more permanent settlement was envisioned. Early communities were formed. The days of hunting and gathering were numbered.

Once the "*fort was made safe*" and the "*family was fed*" in these early communities, a bit of attention could be focused on aesthetics as well. Who was the first saying "*my flowers are taller, and my fruit is plumper*"? Well, to make it official, an Egyptian pharaoh, named

WHAT IS SUSTAINABLE HORTICULTURE?

Lecture Contents (continued)

How Horticulture Helped Shaping Civilization (continued)

Ramses II, proclaimed "*Let there be pleasure gardens*" (1,250 BCE). "*Laden with flowers and fruits from all the lands, with wide open paths ... . A sacred way,*" as he put it.

> *The care of the Earth is our most ancient and most worthy and, after all, our most pleasing responsibility. To foster what remains of it and to foster its renewal is our only legitimate hope.*
>
> —**Wendell Berry**, The Art of the Commons

To "foster the earth's renewal" is a daunting task. Modern civilization often seems intent on *sacrificing the future* to achieve its goals for the present. The Earth's natural systems and its natural resources are in peril on a worldwide basis.

Once productive lands have lost fertility, they are vulnerable to desertification. Productive land is lost to development for human use at an alarming pace. Productive lands are lost to pollution and war caused by human activities. These dangerous trends are exacerbated by climate change and continued population growth.

Fortunately, we are awakening. We humans are at a time of increasing awareness. Water, soil, and resource conservation are of paramount concern. Restoration and rejuvenation of our living environment is critical to human well-being. And horticulturalists, especially those devoted to sustainable practices, play an important role.

Sustainable horticulture entails garden cultivation and plant science based on the principles and practices of Earth stewardship. It is a practice of horticulture with a commitment to foster the Earth's renewal. Sustainable horticulture assures healthy garden cultivation today, with a commitment that future generations will have healthy gardens to cultivate as well. Practitioners of sustainable horticulture create outdoor spaces that benefit human well-being and ecosystem health. They employ practices that are beneficial to the environment, and do not contribute to the depletion of natural resources. Sustainable horticulture supports long-term ecological balance.

Practitioners of sustainable horticulture are keenly aware of water scarcity and water quality. According to the EPA, seven billion gallons of water are used on outdoor landscape needs in the United States *daily*. Half that amount is lost due to runoff, evaporation, and poor design. That is an enormous amount of water, especially when considering the plight of water worldwide. One in nine people on the planet do not have

WHAT IS SUSTAINABLE HORTICULTURE?

Lecture Contents (*continued*)

How Horticulture Helped Shaping Civilization (*continued*)

access to safe and clean drinking water (783 million people). (https://thewaterproject.org/water-scarcity/water_stats).

Rainwater harvest, gray water use, phytoremediation, and stormwater management with living bioswales and permeable hardscapes surfaces are additional methods of sustainable water management strategies that are discussed later in the text.

Practitioners of sustainable horticulture are keenly aware of the importance of soil health, renewal, and conservation. Soil is alive. There are billions of microorganisms in a handful of healthy soil. Each plays a role in the soil ecosystem. Long-term strategies for healthy plants require healthy soil. Yet globally, we have degraded land the equivalent size of the United States and Canada combined.

Hundred million pounds of chemicals are applied to lawns and gardens in the United States annually. These include synthetic fertilizers, synthetic herbicides, and toxic synthetic pesticides. A study by the Center for Disease Control (CDC) tested over 9,000 adults for pesticide and herbicide residue. Based on urine and blood sampling, 100% were contaminated (http://www.headlice.org/news/2004/safelevels.htm).

Synthetic nitrogen fertilizer makes its way into our waterways and causes eutrophication. Eutrophication, in turn, creates harmful algae blooms (HABs). HABs deplete surrounding waters of oxygen in their decay, and create hypoxic waters also known as dead zones. The dead zone in the Gulf of Mexico is currently estimated at 8,776 sq. miles (http://www.noaa.gov/media-release/gulf-of-mexico-dead-zone-is-largest-ever-measured).

Invasive species of plants are a challenging threat to local ecosystems. Nationally, invasive species are the second-greatest threat to endangered species, after habitat destruction (http://www.cal-ipc.org/plants/impact/). Invasive plants increase both the frequency and the severity of wildfire. Invasive plants can alter soil chemistry.

And finally, add air quality to the list of concerns for the sustainable horticulturalist. Again, according to the EPA, pollution from two-stroke-engine landscape and garden maintenance equipment account for 5% of our nation's air pollution. Fifty-five million mowers trim 40 million acres of lawn in the United States annually. More oil and gas are spilled in this endeavor than spilled from the Exxon Valdez in March 1989 (11 million gallons), synthetic chemicals, and soil degradation.

WHAT IS SUSTAINABLE HORTICULTURE?

Lecture Contents (*continued*)

How Horticulture Helped Shaping Civilization (*continued*)

In summary, pursuing sustainable horticulture is no longer optional for human beings. We must do our part to keep the cycle intact, and assure that future generations enjoy the fruits of a healthy functional natural system as well. That is the foundation of sustainable horticulture we seek to build this text upon.

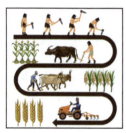

© Hennadii H/Shutterstock. com

History of Horticulture

Prehistoric period—Nomadic hunters and gatherers

- Neolithic Age (20,000 BCE)—Trial and error period of settlement (collection to production)
- Negative effect—100 to 200 plant species in hunter-gatherer's diet reduced to few local growing plants
- Beginning of agriculture (10,000 BCE)—Tigris–Euphrates, Indus, Nile, China, Mesoamerica, East and West Africa

Ancient Egypt (3,500 BCE)

- Domesticated crops
- Gardens with lotus ponds surrounded by date palms and acacia trees
- Natural river irrigation
- Nutrients on top deposited by flood—Light ploughing to break up the top soil
- Gardening in high ground for fruits and vegetables—Fertilizing necessary

The hanging gardens of Babylon

- 2,600 BCE in modern-day Iraq
- Irrigation water lifting system
- ornamental plants for the pleasure of the wife of King Nebuchadnezzar

Ancient Persian garden

- Abundance of water
- Pasargadae Garden by Achaemenian King Cyrus

Lecture Contents (*continued*)

History of Horticulture (*continued*)

Pre-Columbian Central/South America horticulture

- Horticulture beginning between 8,000 and 2,000 BCE
- Aztec, Maya, and Inca civilization
- Vegetables and fruits in irrigated terraces
- Plants for contraception, medicines, dyes, and poison by the Incas
- Horticultural gardens with flowers for Aztec royal class (growing edible plants by lower class)

Greek Hellenic period (750–450 BCE)

- Benefited horticulture through writing (influenced ancient Rome)
- Ideas of enclosure (influences from Persia)

Roman Empire (seventh c BCE—fifth c CE)

- Practical horticulturist—Fruit orchard, flower garden, landscaped garden
- Improved horticultural techniques—Grafting roses, soaking seed before sowing
- Special tools—Pruning knives, ladders

Dark Ages agriculture (fifth c CE–eighth c CE)

- Traditional practice continued—Influence from Islam with new foods and crops
- Monasteries as plant depositories
- Physic gardens of herbs and spices to treat disease and physical ailments (rediscovery of ancient Greek and Rome herbal gardens)
- Herbal lore passed down through generations—Foundation of modern medicine

Middle Ages agriculture (11th c CE–13th c CE)

- Growing population—Expansion of agriculture and horticulture
- Horticultural crops (herbs, vegetables, fruits, flowers) sold, not bartered, as goods
- Influence of city republics based on merchants and commerce—Expansion of trade with the East (spices)
- Formal recognition of horticulture evolved from kitchen garden (edible plants)

WHAT IS SUSTAINABLE HORTICULTURE?

Lecture Contents (*continued*)

© etraveler/Shutterstock.com

Notable Horticulturists

Liberty Hyde Bailey (1858–1954)

- Father of American Horticulture, established land-grant colleges
- https://libertyhydebailey.org/about/about-bailey/

Luther Burbank (1849–1926)

- Pioneer in agricultural science, developed 800+ varieties of plants
- http://www.lutherburbank.org/about-us/luther-burbank

Gertrude Jekyll (1843–1932)

- Horticulturist and garden designer
- https://gertrudejekyll.co.uk/gertrude_jekyll_as_a_plantswoman/

© PardoY/Shutterstock.com

Green Industries

- Segments of nurseries and greenhouses, garden and home center, landscape architects/designers, contractors, maintenance, specialty growers
- Employment growth over the next 5 years in green industries faster than average for all occupation
- Fast growing in *landscape design*, *construction*, and *maintenance* areas—Sustainable and ecologically sound impact on the environment
- *Genetics and biotechnology* to enhance desired aspects and to minimize undesirable
- The US Department of Agriculture (USDA)

© KittyVector/Shutterstock. com

Horticulture as Professionals

- Horticulture as applied science compared to pure science (botany, physics, chemistry, math)
- Pomology (fruit production)—Growing tree fruits as well as small fruits
- Olericulture (vegetable production)—Cultivating all vegetables and crops
- Landscape (environmental) horticulture—Dealing with ornamental plants
- Arboriculture—Tree growing and maintenance
- Turfgrass—Dealing with lawns

WHAT IS SUSTAINABLE HORTICULTURE?

Lecture Contents (*continued*)

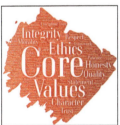

© Madlen/Shutterstock.com

Recreational Horticulture

Horticulture Therapy (Wellness Gardening)

- Horticulture as therapy for physical, intellectual, or emotional disabilities
- Use of multiple senses when growing plants—Potting, transplanting, cutting, watering
- Employment opportunities for people with limited intelligence or physically handicapped

Home Horticulture (Urban Farming)

- Most popular recreational activity—Homegrown vegetables and fruits, gardening
- Necessity of sustained interest in growing plants and information on how to grow
- *Cooperative Extension Services*—Great source of gardening (https://ucanr.edu/About/Locations/)

© design36/Shutterstock.com

Code of Ethics and Conducts

- Natural approach—Protecting the welfare of nature
- Social and environmental responsibility
- Natural capital—Valuable products or services in the future (recycling, water conservation, erosion control, etc.)
- Utilitarian approach—Multiple perspectives and solutions for the greatest good
- Rights approach—The right to choose paths
- Common good approach—Benefit to all members of the community

WHAT IS SUSTAINABLE HORTICULTURE?

Relevant Links

Wikipedia (Reference purpose only)
    Horticulture   https://en.wikipedia.org/wiki/Horticulture
    Sustainability   https://en.wikipedia.org/wiki/Sustainability
    Sustainable Agriculture   https://en.wikipedia.org/wiki/Sustainable_agriculture
    Sustainable Gardening   https://en.wikipedia.org/wiki/Sustainable_gardening

American Society of Horticulture Science
    Certified Professional Horticulturist   https://www.ashs.org/page/CPH?

The Water Project
    Facts About Water   https://thewaterproject.org/water-scarcity/water_stats

Environmental Media Services
    "Pesticide Body Burden"   http://www.headlice.org/news/2004/safelevels.htm

National Oceanic and Atmospheric
  Administration
    Gulf of Mexico "Dead Zone"   http://www.noaa.gov/media-release/gulf-of-mexico-dead-zone-is-largest-ever-measured

California Invasive Plants Council
    About Invasive Plants   https://www.cal-ipc.org/plants/impact/

WHAT IS SUSTAINABLE HORTICULTURE?

Quizzes

© Davidovka/Shutterstock. com

1. Describe the definition of horticulture, including three examples of primary subjects. What is the difference between agriculture and horticulture?

2. Describe the definition of sustainability, including three examples of being sustainable.

3. What are three main elements to make horticulture sustainable?

FUNDAMENTALS OF HORTICULTURE

PLANT CLASSIFICATION AND BOTANICAL NOMENCLATURE

Relevant Words

American Horticulture Society (AHS), Angiosperms, Binomial nomenclature, *Carl Linnaeus*, Classification, Cotyledon, Cultivar, Dicots, Dioecious, Electromagnetic radiation, Epithet, Evaporation rate, Genus, Gymnosperms, International Botanical Congress (IBC), International Code of Nomenclature (ICN), Monocots, Monoecious, Pistil, Plant Hardiness Zone Map, Plant Heat Zone Map, Precipitation, Stamen, United States Department of Agriculture (USDA)

Lab Objective

To learn about plant classification, taxonomy, and botanical nomenclature.

Lab Assignment

From your favorite plants identified in previous chapter lab assignment

- Identify each plant with its botanical naming nomenclature and common name.
- Find a plant with the similar botanical name, and, compare it with the original one, identifying the similarity and difference.

Lecture Outlines

© alinabel/Shutterstock.com

- ❖ Plant Classification, Taxonomy, and Botanical Nomenclature
- ❖ Contribution of *Carl Linnaeus*
- ❖ Climate and Hardiness Zones

PLANT CLASSIFICATION AND BOTANICAL NOMENCLATURE

Lecture Contents

© alinabel/Shutterstock.com

Plant Classification

Classification is the orderly grouping of things according to shared qualities or characteristics. It is a process borne from observation and experience. We learn this way, and more importantly, we share information this way. We place something in a category, to enable a better understanding of it.

Some movies are classified with a rating of "G." If a movie is in that group, we can be fairly confident the film will be appropriate for all audiences, including children. If a movie is classified with a rating of "R," we know it is a completely different deal. We classify clothes as business attire or casual. We categorize cars as fast or slow or somewhere in between. We classify king-size sheets or queen. We group insects as beneficial insects or pests. The list of lists is daunting.

Since early times, humans have initiated the same process of categorizing and grouping things, and it was especially important with plants. We came to learn of plants that we could eat and ones that we definitely could not. We found groups of medicinal plants for all kinds of ailments. We observed groups of plants that could be used for products, dyes, oils, and even lethal concoctions.

As scientists and scholars began to classify plants, they did so first, based on the reproductive method of the plant of concern. Hence, plants were divided into two distinct groups: the seed-bearing and non-seed-bearing. The non-seed-bearing plants are reproduced via spores, such as mosses and ferns. While of much importance to botany, non-seed-bearing plants are not the subject of this text.

Seed-bearing plants include those with a "naked" seed (the gymnosperms) and those with an enclosed seed (the angiosperms). The gymnosperms include the cone-bearing (coniferous) trees of pine, fir, cedar, spruce, and many others, and while important in forestry and landscape design, they are not considered in depth in this text.

Angiosperms are the "flowering" plants, which comprise plants from vegetables to grasses, to flowers, trees, and shrubs commonly used in gardens, urban farms, and landscape designs. Angiosperms are divided into monocotyledonous plants (monocots) and dicotyledonous plants (dicots). These plants are categorized by the number of cotyledon inside the seed (a cotyledon is the energy source for a seed).

PLANT CLASSIFICATION AND BOTANICAL NOMENCLATURE

Lecture Contents (*continued*)

Plant Classification (*continued*)

Plants are grouped according to the number of male parts (stamen) and number of female parts (pistil). They can be grouped by the number of petals and the number of seeds inside the fruit. Plants can be grouped by use (medicinal, therapeutic, edible, and ornamental). Plants can be grouped by origin (native vs. exotic, Mediterranean, tropical, etc.) Plants can be grouped by their life cycle (perennial, annual, biennial, and monocarp).

Plants can be grouped by their pollination requirements: monoecious (having the male and female flower parts in one plant) versus dioecious (having the male and female flower parts in separate plants). Plants can be grouped as to whether they are evergreen (retaining their leaves) or deciduous (dropping the leaves seasonally). Plants can be grouped on whether they are woody, succulent, or herbaceous (fleshy). They can be grouped according to their growth habit (ground cover, shrub, or tree). Again, the list is extensive.

Classifying plants brings needed order to the vast variety of plants in the world. Knowing that a relationship exists between two or more plants gives one clues about other similarities that might exist, such as hardiness, growth rate, soil preference, and climate needs. Classifying a plant can help us know the correct care of a plant.

PLANT CLASSIFICATION AND BOTANICAL NOMENCLATURE

Lecture Contents (*continued*)

Plant Classification (*continued*)

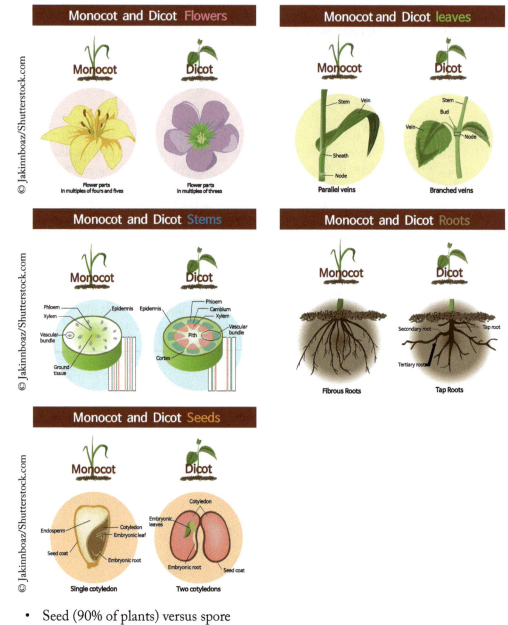

- Seed (90% of plants) versus spore
- *Gymnosperms* (ex. pines) vs. *Angiosperms* (ex. Flowers)

PLANT CLASSIFICATION AND BOTANICAL NOMENCLATURE

Lecture Contents (*continued*)

Plant Classification (*continued*)

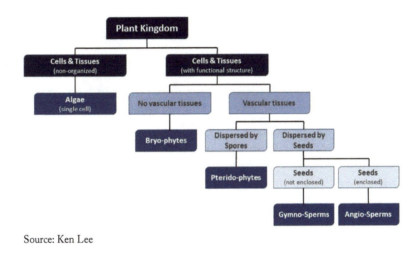

Source: Ken Lee

© Cat_arch_angel/
Shutterstock.com

Botanical Nomenclature

Early on, groupings of plants were described (or classified) in partial sentences or even a short paragraph. "A rambling climbing perennial with compound leaves and red petals" might have been used to describe a climbing rose, for example. This was cumbersome and confusing.

An orderly system of naming groups of plants (and individual species) became increasingly necessary with the rise of global exploration and trade. In 1753, a Swedish physician–botanist–zoologist named Carl Linnaeus introduced a two-name system to describe plants. It was proposed that this system be universal. And it was proposed that the names be in Latin (because that was the leading science language at the time.)

Linnaeus described how plants should be classified with binomial nomenclature (a "two-words" system) in his book titled *Species Plantarum*. Linnaeus proposed that one part of a plant's name would consist of a general group in which they fall (the genus). The second of two words would describe the specific plant itself (the specific epithet). The specific epithet can describe the plant's appearance and growth characteristics, its use, its scent, its discoverer, its place of origin, and more. *Sequoia giganteum*, for example, is the Latin name

PLANT CLASSIFICATION AND BOTANICAL NOMENCLATURE

Lecture Contents (*continued*)

Botanical Nomenclature (*continued*)

for a tree native to California, the giant sequoia. Sequoia is the group to which this tree belongs (the genus) and the specific epithet (*giganteum*) describes the tree's massive girth.

This method of naming plants became popular and widely accepted. Linnaeus named over 5,000 plants in his book. And 5 years later, he wrote *Systema Naturae*, and proposed that animals be named in the same fashion. His system for naming plants and animals remains universally accepted.

Today the set of rules governing the use of botanical names is found within the International Code of Nomenclature (ICN) for algae, fungi, and plants. The ICN, in turn, is overseen by the International Botanical Congress (IBC). The IBC is a group of plant scientists that meets every 6 years. The first annual IBC was held in 1864 in Brussels, Belgium, in conjunction with an international horticultural exhibit.

The most recent meeting of the IBC was in 2017 in Shenzhen, China (http://www. ibc2017.cn/About/). The next IBC event will be held in Rio de Janeiro, Brazil, during July 2023.

The IBC has established rules governing the use of the binomial nomenclature system. The genus must be capitalized. The specific epithet must be all lowercase. The entire botanic or scientific name given to a plant must be italicized. If it is handwritten, the botanic name must be underlined.

Exceptions occur in nature. If a plant is a naturally occurring exception (i.e., the plant can be found growing naturally in the wild, and its seed will reproduce the same form), the plant is termed a variety. Examples include a weeping habit, a double flower instead of single, or a different color leaf.

The variety name always follows the specific epithet, are written entirely in lower case, and are italicized (or underlined if handwritten). *Acer palmatum* is the botanic name given to Japanese maple. *Acer palmatum atropurpureum* has a naturally occurring variation; it has red leaves instead of green. This "mutation" occurs in the wild and seeds collected will bear a tree with the same red leaves, so it is termed a variety.

PLANT CLASSIFICATION AND BOTANICAL NOMENCLATURE

Lecture Contents (continued)

Botanical Nomenclature (continued)

A cultivar, on the other hand, is an exception as well, but does not reoccur naturally in the wild. Cultivar is short for cultivated variety, meaning human hands have intervened. We reproduce such plants, if they are desirable, through asexual reproduction methods (discussed later in Chapter 6.

A cultivar must be written with single quotation marks. *Acer rubrum* is the red maple. *Acer rubrum 'Autumn Flame'* is a red maple cultivar with brilliant fall color.

Every word used to describe a plant comprises one or more morphemes. The following chart shows some commonly used morphemes and/or plants whose common names are Latin (Iris, Chrysanthemum, etc.)

Unit	Example
Kingdom	Plant
Division	Tracheophyta (vascular plants)
Subdivision	Pteropsida (ferns and seed-bearing plants)
Class	Angiosperms (flowering plants)
Sub-class	Dicotyledones
Order	Rosales
Family	Rosaceae
Genus	Rosa
Species	Rugosa
Variety/Cultivar	'Alba'

- Orderly classification and naming of plants (taxonomy)
- Expressed in Latin for being universal and precise
- *Carl Linnaeus*, the founder of taxonomy (https://ucmp.berkeley.edu/history/linnaeus.html)
- Plant species = *genus* + *epithet*; for example, *Ceanothus cyaneus* (Sierra Blue Ceanothus)
- *Variety (var)* (natural mutation) versus *cultivar (cv)* (man-made)

PLANT CLASSIFICATION AND BOTANICAL NOMENCLATURE

Lecture Contents (*continued*)

© Katerina Davidenko/
Shutterstock.com

Climate and Hardiness Zones

Will an avocado tree survive (outdoors) in Wyoming? Unfortunately, not. Its winters are too cold. Will a sour cherry tree survive in Arizona? Not cold enough! Obviously, a horticulturalist must know enough about a plant to know that it can survive and flourish. We start by identifying what is called a plant's climate zone.

In geographic terms, there are three major climate zones on the Earth consisting of the polar, temperate, and tropical zones. Temperatures in these three climate zones are determined mainly by the location, or latitude, of the zone. The coldest temperatures are found in the polar zone, where it is almost always below freezing. The temperate zone is characterized by cold winters, warm summers, and moderate spring and fall seasons. Tropical zones remain a constant warm temperature, with little fluctuation day and night.

In horticultural terms, climate zones are defined by the United States Department of Agriculture (USDA) and by the American Horticulture Society (AHS). Each agency produces a map that differentiates regions of the country based on how cold or how hot the climate is.

The USDA map is known as the Plant Hardiness Zone Map. It shows the average annual minimum temperatures in a region. The map shows just how cold it gets, with Zone 1 being the coldest (−50°F), and Zone 11 being the warmest (where it only gets as low as 40°F). Again, the avocado tree, for example, is classified as being hardy (can survive) in Zones 9 to 10. There are no Zones 9 to 10 in Wyoming. The tree is thus not recommended there.

There is a slight limitation with relying solely on the USDA map. Cold hardiness is not the only factor that affects a plant's ability to thrive. Take, for example, the average annual minimum temperatures in the Olympic National Forest (in the Pacific Northwest) and the Sonoran Desert (in the American southwest). It rarely gets below freezing in parts of either, so parts of these environments would be classified in the same USDA Zone.

The two environments are vastly different and have a dramatic effect on which plants can survive in each locale. Obviously, the desert exposure is significantly hotter and drier.

The AHS developed the Plant Heat Zone Map as part of the answer. It shows the average number of days per year above 86°F, or just how hot it gets. Zone 1 has less than 1 hot day in excess of 86 (on the average). Zone 12, according to the AHS map, has more than 210 days per year at 86°F or higher.

Lecture Contents (*continued*)

Climate and Hardiness Zones (*continued*)

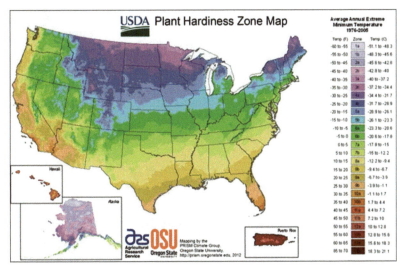

Source: USDA.gov, http://planthardiness.ars.usda.gov/PHZMWeb/.

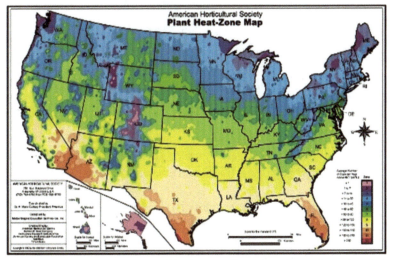

Source: Reproduced with permission of the American Horticultural Society (www.ahsgardening.org.), http://ahsgardening.org/gardening-resources/gardening-maps/heat-zone-map.

PLANT CLASSIFICATION AND BOTANICAL NOMENCLATURE

Lecture Contents (*continued*)

© Lustra Frisk/Shutterstock. com

Elements of Climate

When we discuss weather, we focus on what it's like outside right now, or perhaps we look at a forecast for the week ahead. When we talk about weather, it is relative tvo a short period of time. When we talk about climate, we discuss the long-term pattern of weather in a region. Climate scientists analyze data of 30 years or more.

A description of climate must include the elements of temperature, precipitation, humidity, wind, and light. These five elements of climate affect plant growth, and, are examined below.

Temperature is a description of hot and cold that can be measured with a thermometer. The coldest recorded temperature on earth (–128.6°F) was recorded at an Antarctic research station in 1983 (https://www.usatoday.com/story/weather/2018/01/17/oymya-kon-yakutia-siberia-russia-extreme-cold-temperatures/1039929001/). The hottest ever verified was 134.1°F in Death Valley, California, in 1913 (http://www.guinnessworldrecords.com/world-records/highest-recorded-temperature/).

Obviously, plants are generally better off somewhere in between these two extremes. As referred to previously, a plant thrives at an optimal temperature for which the species originated from and has adapted to (i.e., an avocado tree doesn't survive in cold places).

Precipitation is water that forms in the atmosphere and falls to the earth in the form of rain, snow, hail, sleet, and ice. Plants need water for various functions, including photosynthesis, for which it is a critical ingredient. Their water needs vary regionally of course, and by species. Some plants are thirsty, and some are not. Some have adapted to near-drought and/or desert conditions. Others thrive among the rainforests of the world.

Precipitation rates vary widely across the globe. *Mawsynram* is a village in India that receives 12 meters (470 inches) of rain annually. It is the wettest place on earth (www.worldatlas.com/articles/the-ten-wettest-places-in-the-world.html).

The driest place on Earth is in Antarctica in an area called the Dry Valleys, which have seen no rain for nearly 2 million years (www.universetoday.com/15031/driest-place-on-earth/).

Humidity describes the amount of water in its gaseous state, in the air surrounding us (water vapor). When humidity is high, air is saturated with a high volume of water vapor molecules. Much like a full sponge, highly humid air won't absorb much more water. Thus, humidity

PLANT CLASSIFICATION AND BOTANICAL NOMENCLATURE

Lecture Contents (*continued*)

Elements of Climate (*continued*)

affects evaporation. When humidity is high, evaporation rates will fall. When evaporation rates fall, the phenomenon of water movement in a plant falls as well.

This process (of water movement in a plant) is termed as transpiration. Moisture is carried from the roots of the plant to small openings on the underside of the leaves (the stomata) and is released to the atmosphere as water vapor. This keeps the process of water movement going (see section "Transpiration" in Chapter 4).

Humidity levels affect when and how plants open the stomata. When the weather is hot, or drought conditions exist, a plant may close its stomata to reduce water losses. If kept closed for long periods of time, the plants' ability to "breathe" is diminished. It has no way to consume carbon dioxide (a critical ingredient in photosynthesis) and release the oxygen produced (a critical gas we breathe).

Wind is the horizontal movement of air from one location to another. It's measured in knots and described as breeze, gust, gale, or squall. Wind can be mild or fierce, with a corresponding impact on plant adaptation, vigor, and survival.

Wind is created because the different surfaces of the earth absorb heat differently, which creates differences in air pressure. And in nature, air flows from areas of higher pressure to areas of lower pressure, like air being released from a balloon.

Certain plants rely on wind for pollination. Light winds help a young plant develop sturdy limbs. Other times winds rip plants from the ground—large trees included. Wind has a definite impact on plant health, growth characteristics, and survival.

Light is a form of kinetic energy that travels in oscillating waves called electromagnetic radiation. It plays a critical role in plant health. Sunlight intensity, light quality, and day length (photoperiod) directly affect photosynthesis, which is how a plant makes energy for itself, and for animals that consume it.

Light quality refers to the specific wavelengths of light; light intensity is the degree of brightness that a plant receives; and day length is the duration of the day with respect to the night period (photosynthesis is discussed in Chapter 4).

PLANT CLASSIFICATION AND BOTANICAL NOMENCLATURE

Relevant Links

TEDTalk
Hidden Miracles of the Natural World

https://www.ted.com/talks/louie_schwartzberg_hidden_
miracles_of_the_natural_world

United States Department of Agriculture
Plant Hardiness
Classification

http://planthardiness.ars.usda.gov/PHZMWeb/#
https://plants.usda.gov/classification.html

American Horticultural Society
Heat Zone

http://ahsgardening.org/gardening-resources/gardening-maps/
heat-zone-map

Sunset Magazine
Climate Zone

http://www.sunset.com/garden/climate-zones/climate-
zones-intro-us-map

Burpee
Growing Zone

http://www.burpee.com/gardening/content/gygg/
growing-zone-information/growingzoneinfo.html

PLANT CLASSIFICATION AND BOTANICAL NOMENCLATURE

Quizzes

1. Fill in the blank from the following statement:

   _____ are the "flowering" plants, which comprise plants from vegetables to grasses, to flowers, trees, and shrubs commonly used in gardens, urban farms, and landscape designs. _____ are divided into monocotyledonous plants called _____ and dicotyledonous plants called _____.

2. Name two organizations that set the rules governing the use of botanical names.

3. Name two maps that may be used for identifying plant's appropriate growing zone in the United States.

Relevant Words

Anther, Calyx, Chlorophyll, Chloroplasts, Complete flower, Compound leaf, Corolla, Corymb, Cyme, Dichotomous venation, Filament, Inflorescence, Leaf venation, Margin, Mesophyll, Morphology, Ovary, Palmate vernation, Panicle, Pedicel, Peduncle, Perfect flower, Pericarp, Petals, Petiole, Phloem, Photosynthesis, Phytomorphology, Pinnate, Pistil, Sepals, Sessile, Solitary flower, Spike, Stamen, Stigma, Style, Raceme, Umbel, Xylem

Lab Objective

To identify and to learn about a plant's external elements.

Lab Assignment

From your favorite plants identified in previous lab assignment

- Describe the components of each plant, such as leaf, flower, branch, and trunk, as detailed as possible with your own observation. If helpful, take the photos or sketch them.
- Describe the detailed flower structure.
- Differentiate each plant with *gymnosperms versus angiosperms, monocot versus dicot,* and *seed-bearing versus spore-bearing*

Lecture Outlines

© Kazakova Maryia/
Shutterstock.com

❖ Plant Morphology—External Parts: Roots, Stems, Leaves
❖ Flowers and Fruits

CHAPTER 2

PLANT MORPHOLOGY

Lecture Contents

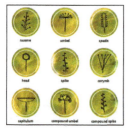

© Alena Dubinets/
Shutterstock.com

Plant Morphology

The study of plant anatomy is the study of a plant's internal structure. Plant morphology (sometimes referred as phytomorphology) is the study of a plant's external parts and their function. Study of a plant's external parts is of significant aid in plant identification. Roots, stems, leaves, flowers, and fruits are each examined in the following sections.

Stems support the plant. At the juvenile stage, the plant's stems begin to strengthen, stiffen, and elongate. They support the plant under the weight of its leaves, flowers, and eventually fruit. They support the plant against the weight of rain, sleet, ice, snow, wind, and even errant soccer balls.

Stems also house "the plumbing" of the plant, which consists of a bundle of vascular cells called the xylem and phloem cells. They act much as veins and arteries are to animals. Water and nutrients from the soil are transported throughout the plant via the xylem. The products of photosynthesis (sugars) are transported throughout the plant via the phloem.

When leaves form, they are arranged along the stem with precision in a manner to maximize photosynthesis. Sometimes they are arranged opposite one another along the stem. We call such arrangement an opposite arrangement.

When leaves are not opposite, but are instead staggered along the stem, we term such arrangement as an alternate leaf arrangement. It can be a means to identify a species; it is a plant-identifying characteristic or clue.

And finally, when leaves join the stem at a common point around the stem, they are deemed to be a whorled arrangement. Leaves are quite diverse when shape, size, texture, and color are considered, but not so much when considering their purpose: food, medicines, habitat, shade and cooling, erosion control, and a multitude of products.

More significantly, leaves are an important part of the plant because it is through its leaves that a plant is able to absorb the energy from the sun in the process of photosynthesis.

Note the entire leaf consists of the leaf stalk (if present) and the leaf blade together. The stalk of a single leaf is called the petiole. If the petiole is absent, the leaf is said to be sessile (Latin "without stalk").

PLANT MORPHOLOGY

Lecture Contents (*continued*)

Plant Morphology (*continued*)

The edge of the leaf is called the margin. The margin might be smooth, and without indentation, which is termed an entire margin. Margin types include barbed, dentate (toothed), incised (cut), lobed, undulate (wavy), ciliate (hairy), and others.

The tip of the leaf (apex) and the base of the leaf (base) are also identifying characteristics. The apex might be abrupt (terminating suddenly) or acute (tapering to a point). The base could be equal sided (equilateral) or oblique.

Leaf venation refers to the pattern of "veins" in the leaf blade. The veins are continuation of the bundles of xylem and phloem. They also offer structural support to the leaf blade as well.

The midrib is the central support structure of the leaf, often located longitudinally along the middle of the leaf blade. When the central midrib has "veins" spaced along the midrib, the leaf is said to have pinnate (Latin "like a feather") venation. If three or more midribs are joined at a common point at the base of the blade, the leaf is said to have palmate venation.

In parallel venation, the veins are all smaller in size and parallel or nearly parallel to one another along the leaf blade, with a series of smaller veins interconnecting each.

Dichotomous venation refers to the pattern where the venation is branched into two mostly equal divisions (like the branches of a tree), with venation running mostly parallel in one "branch" in one direction and running the opposite direction in the other "branch."

The central tissues of a leaf between the upper and lower epidermis are called the mesophyll. Chlorophyll, which is the green pigment of plants associated with photosynthesis, resides there in the mesophyll, in organelles called the chloroplasts.

Leaves that occur individually are termed as simple leaves. Leaves that occur in clusters are known as compound leaves. The absence of a bud at the intersection of leaf indicates one is examining a leaflet (rather than leaf) and the leaflet is thus considered part of a compound leaf.

A compound leaf is pinnately compound if the leaflets are arranged in a pattern similar "as a feather." Twice pinnate, with the divisions again pinnately divided, is termed bipinnately compound.

PLANT MORPHOLOGY

Lecture Contents (*continued*)

Plant Morphology (*continued*)

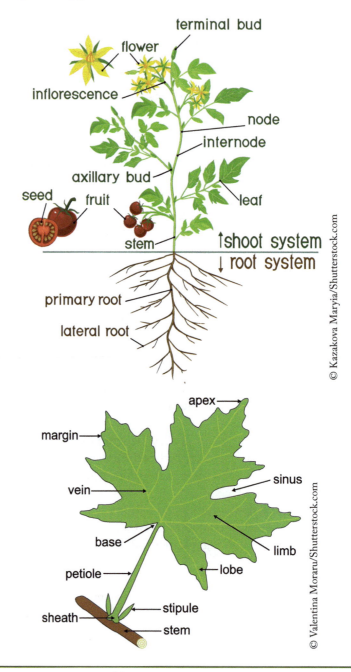

PLANT MORPHOLOGY

Lecture Contents (*continued*)

Plant Morphology (*continued*)

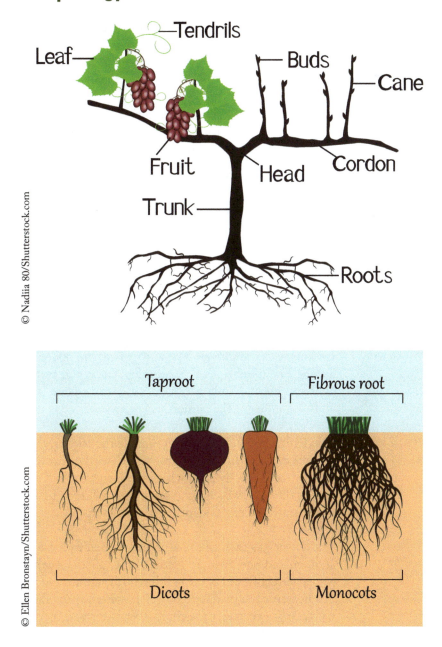

© Nadiia 80/Shutterstock.com

© Ellen Bronstayn/Shutterstock.com

Lecture Contents (*continued*)

© leonori/Shutterstock.com

Flower and Fruit

Flowers, like leaves, are quite diverse. They vary in size, shape, color, and scent. Upon close examination, one will find that they vary in many other details as well. Still, the purpose of each flower is the same, and that is reproduction; a continuance and improvement of the species.

For reproduction to take place, a plant must have flowers containing male parts and female parts. If the male and female parts are in the same flower, then the flower is said to be *a perfect flower*. Flower parts of a perfect and complete flower are examined later.

A flower bud is most often covered in its developing stage, to protect it from environmental elements and biological threats (the developing flower could be eaten, frozen, or scorched, to name a few). The covering on a perfect and complete flower is called the *calyx* (Latin for "covering"). The calyx comprises individual *sepals*. The calyx (and its sepals) protects the developing flower until it unfurls. The *corolla* is then revealed, which comprises individual *petals*. The corolla (with its petals) is there to attract pollinators.

The male parts of the flower include the *anther* and *filament*. Collectively, these parts are known as the *stamen.* The anther is where pollen is held. The filament supports the anther. The number, size, positioning, color, and texture of the stamens are identifying characteristics of a plant. You can identify a plant, for example, by the positioning of, and/or number of the anthers.

The female parts of the flower include the *stigma, style*, and *ovary(ies)*, which together comprise the *pistil*. The stigma serves as the "landing pad" for pollen. The stigma is supported by the style (in which a pollen tube will form upon pollination). The ovary houses the eggs, which upon successful pollination, will become seeds. The positioning of the pistil is a plant-identifying characteristic.

If a flower has each of the aforementioned four parts (a calyx, a corolla, one or more stamen, and one or more pistils), it is called a *complete flower*. A complete flower is also a perfect flower because it has both stamen and pistil. Note that a perfect flower is not necessarily a complete flower, however. If the flower is lacking a calyx (as in tulip) or lacking a corolla, then the flower is termed incomplete. A tulip is an incomplete, perfect flower.

PLANT MORPHOLOGY

Lecture Contents (*continued*)

Flower and Fruit (*continued*)

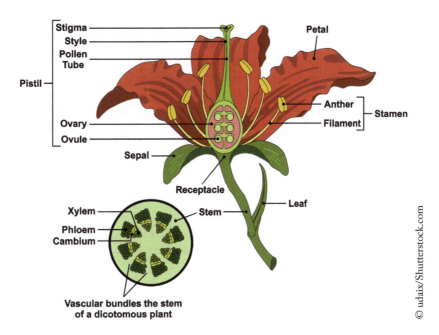

The stalk of an individual flower, or of a cluster of flowers, is called the peduncle. If a flower (or floret) does not have a stalk, it is said to be a sessile flower.

A single flower on a peduncle is called a **solitary flower.** A cluster of flowers on a peduncle is called an **inflorescence**. Each flower in an inflorescence is borne on a small stalk attached to the peduncle, which is termed a **pedicel,** (unless, of course, the flowers in the cluster are sessile).

Numerous inflorescence types are spike like, while others have a spherical or flat top. A **spike** is an inflorescence in the shape of a spike, but whose flowers are sessile. A **raceme** is like a spike, except the flowers are not sessile (each has a pedicel). A **panicle** is a branched raceme.

A **head** is a spherical or flat-topped inflorescence whose flowers are sessile (as is the sunflower). An **umbel** is a flat or spherical topped inflorescence whose flowers attach to the peduncle at a common point (like an inside-out umbrella). A geranium's flowers are formed in an umbel.

Lecture Contents (*continued*)

Flower and Fruit (*continued*)

Corymbs and *cymes* resemble umbels, but the flower's pedicels attach at a different point along the top of the peduncle. The difference between a corymb and cyme is in the pattern in which the flowers bloom. In a corymb, the flowers in the middle of the inflorescence bloom last. In a cyme, the flowers in the middle of the inflorescence bloom first.

In the culinary (food) arts, a fruit is something that can be eaten raw or fresh and is generally sweet. Botanically and horticulturally speaking, a *fruit* is the seed-bearing organ of a flowering plant. Flowering plants produce fruit. An acorn is a fruit. It is the fruit of the oak flower (*Quercus spp.*). A kernel of corn is the fruit of a corn flower. A tomato is also a fruit. Simply stated, if it bears seed (and is from a flowering plant), it is indeed a fruit.

Fruits are a means by which the plant can disseminate its seeds. Some are "packaged" in bright red berries to make them attractive for mammals to consume. A bear will eat berries and travel far before the seeds are dispersed. A bur is a fruit that has hooks on its barbs. The bur attaches to an animal fur and is widely dispersed. Coconut fruits can float thousands of miles in the ocean before the coconut seed is dispersed.

Some fruits are dry and hard, like the acorn. Others are fleshy and succulent, like a watermelon. Some split open at maturity (dehiscent), and some remain closed (indehiscent). The outermost layer of the fruit is called the *pericarp*.

Fruits can be simple, or they can be multiple, and/or aggregate. *Simple* fruits result from the ripening of a flower with only one pistil, such as a cherry or apple. *Aggregate* fruits develop from a single flower with numerous pistils, like a raspberry or strawberry. A *multiple* fruit is formed from an inflorescence, where each flower produces a fruit, but these mature into a single mass, as in the pineapple.

<table>
<tr><td></td><td></td></tr>
</table>

CHAPTER 2	PLANT MORPHOLOGY

Relevant Links

TEDTalk

World's Oldest Living Things

https://www.ted.com/talks/rachel_sussman_the_world_s_oldest_living_things?utm_campaign=tedspread&utm_medium=referral&utm_source=tedcomshare

Why We're Storing Billons of Seeds

https://www.ted.com/talks/jonathan_drori_why_we_re_storing_billions_of_seeds?utm_campaign=tedspread&utm_medium=referral&utm_source=tedcomshare

Garden in My Apartment

https://www.ted.com/talks/britta_riley_a_garden_in_my_apartment?utm_campaign=tedspread&utm_medium=referral&utm_source=tedcomshare

Wiki (Reference purpose only)

Plant Morphology   https://en.wikipedia.org/wiki/Plant_morphology

Flower   https://en.wikipedia.org/wiki/Flower

PLANT MORPHOLOGY

Quizzes

1. Identify at least three elements of plant's anatomy.

2. The edge of the leaf is called the margin. Describe different types of leaf margin (at least four).

3. A complete flower is a perfect flower. And, a perfect flower is also a complete flower. True or False?

GERMINATION AND PLANT LIFE CYCLE

Relevant Words

Cotyledon, Endosperm, Epigeous germination, Germination, Hypocotyl, Hypogeous, Imbibition, Radicle, Scarification

Lab Objective

To identify and to learn about seed types and germination process.

Lab Assignment

- Visit a local nursery and purchase the seeds for your favorites of edible and flower.
- Research the recommended sowing process for the seeds selected.
- Sow the seeds per your findings, and make the detailed records of sowing process.
- Describe the stages of dormancy, senescence, and abscission.
- List four plant hormones and their principle effects.

Lecture Outlines

© Pensiri/Shutterstock.com

- ❖ Germination/Dissemination
- ❖ Scarification
- ❖ Understanding Plant Life Cycles: *Annuals Versus Perennials*
- ❖ Work of *Gregor Mendel* on the Principles of Genetics
- ❖ Phenomenon of Hybrid Vigor

GERMINATION AND PLANT LIFE CYCLE

Lecture Contents

© Bogdan Wankowicz/
Shutterstock.com

Germination

As in nature, let's start with the seed. Here we see a part of the plant that appears neither alive nor dead. It is neither; seeds are dormant. They remain dormant until favorable conditions exist, then sprout with new life in the process called germination.

A seed has everything it needs to survive dormancy and spring forth to life. It has a seed coat to protect it from organisms and extremes, such as drought, freeze, and/or scorch before germination. It has energy within to fuel the process of growth and development (through its cotyledons and endosperm). It has instructions (in the form of its DNA) to guide the plant with its growth and pending life cycle.

Genetics

Plant traits are passed on in plants, as they are in animals, from parent to offspring. Seed from a maple tree will produce a maple tree of similar characteristics, including size, shape, color, disease resistance, and so on.

These plant traits are held in the plant's DNA. DNA is a complex molecule. It is the carrier of genetic information; a molecular blueprint for a living thing. It is a bunch of atoms stuck together to form a long spiraling ladder.

Genes, in turn, are large chunks of DNA, residing in the nucleus of each cell. Traits are passed on in plants in the form of genes. The genes provide the instructions on what the plant is, what it looks like, how it is to survive, and how it will interact with its surrounding environment.

The characteristics of an offspring are dependent upon contribution of traits from both parents. Genes have a quality known as dominate or recessive. When you cross a red flower with a white flower (of the same species), you do not get a pink flower. You get a number of red flowers, and an occasional white flower. It depends on the dominant or recessive traits in the DNA. It's the same with animals, including humans. Your dad may have had black hair, and somehow your hair is blond.

Gregor Mendel (1822–1840) was a Swiss monk who had a passion for studying genetics: the study of heredity and the variation of inherited characteristics. Initially, he studied rabbits. But those higher up at the monastery suggested that was too much about sex. He was a monk after all.

GERMINATION AND PLANT LIFE CYCLE

Lecture Contents (*continued*)

Germination (*continued*)

> So, Gregor Mendel studied the genetics of plants instead. He grew over 42,000 pea plants in his years of study. It was Gregor Mendel, the father of Genetics, who discovered the role of genes in heredity. Critics widely dismissed his work. It was not until after Mendel's death that his findings would be accepted, yet it is almost common knowledge today.

The phenomenon of Hybrid Vigor

> Hybrid vigor, or heterosis, refers to the increased hardiness and improved function of an organism due to genetic diversity. "An offspring exhibits heterosis if its traits are enhanced as a result of mixing the genetic contributions of its parents" (*https://www.britannica.com/science/heterosis*).

> Most are familiar that "inbreeding" causes weaknesses in the gene pool. When a population is small or inbred, it tends to lose genetic diversity. Hybrid vigor is the opposite. Organisms benefit from outbreeding whether plant or animal. Outbreeding provides for enhancement of the species. If a tomato is cross-pollinated with one that has a degree of proven cold hardiness, we are likely to get a new improved tomato with increased hardiness. We improve them for taste, size, rate of growth, durability, color, and other such enhancements.

Each seed has an embryonic plant inside, whether it is a coconut (a large seed) or the earth's smallest seed, barely visible without a microscope. The tiny plant reveals its stem and leaves, which are tucked within, in a kind of fetal position.

The seed comes complete with its own power supply as well. Until a plant has developed its leaves above surface, it cannot photosynthesize; it cannot get its needed energy from the sun. Instead, the germinating seed relies on bundles of energy in the seed called *cotyledon(s)* and/or *endosperm*.

The word cotyledon stems from the Greek word "*kotyl*," meaning "hollow, cavity" or "concave." When you look at two "halves" of a peanut seed, you are actually examining the seed's two cotyledons (note the indentations). Dicots have two cotyledons. Monocots have one.

Upon germination, the cotyledon usually becomes the embryonic first leaves of a seedling. Other times the cotyledon simply withers as its energy reserves are exhausted.

GERMINATION AND PLANT LIFE CYCLE

Lecture Contents (*continued*)

Germination (*continued*)

In any case, if the cotyledons (or the cotyledon leaves) remain attached and are visible after the seedling emerges from the soil, the germination process is termed *epigeous germination* (from the words epic [above] and geo [earth]). If the cotyledon remains below the surface, then the germination process is termed *hypogeous* ("under earth").

The favorable conditions that lead to germination are (1) optimal temperature, (2) optimal moisture, and (3) ample oxygen. Here, optimal is a key word. Desert plant seeds require prolonged heat; alpine plant seeds will remain relatively cool during germination. Excess moisture might leave certain seed species nonviable. In other species, lack of moisture thwarts germination instead.

Once favorable conditions are achieved, the seed coat must deteriorate, diminish, or be compromised; there must be a means for water to be absorbed for germination to commence. This initial process is called *scarification*.

There are several means by which a seed coat is scarified. A seed is blown by wind through a rocky canyon and its seed coat is nicked and scraped. We can duplicate this in lab or greenhouse with a coffee can and heavy grit sandpaper (shake, shake, shake . . .). We can mimic nature in this regard with a nick from a knife or other small tool.

Seed coats are scarified by the acid in the intestines of birds and other animals who eat the seeds and fruit. When the seed passes through the animal and is dispersed, the seed coat is diminished and ready to absorb the optimal moisture mentioned earlier. We can mimic this process in lab with dilution of sulfuric acid.

The seed coat of some species requires the heat of fire (and/or chemicals from the smoke) for scarification, and of course we can duplicate these processes. Other seed types are scarified by the presence of soil microorganisms "chewing" through the seed coat. Other species by the simple dissolvent by water as well.

After the seed coat is scarified, water is absorbed in a process called *imbibition*. When the seed takes on water in this process, it splits, and an embryonic root emerges, to anchor the seed. The embryonic root is termed the *radicle*.

In a monocot (grasses, palms and such), only the leaves emerge from the seed. In a dicot, the stem elongates with the leaves, navigating its way toward the surface with

GERMINATION AND PLANT LIFE CYCLE

Lecture Contents (*continued*)

Germination (*continued*)

ease and precision. The embryonic stem tip (still holding the cotyledons) is called the *hypocotyl*.

When leaves emerge from the hypocotyl, the plant will begin photosynthesis. The energy reserves in the cotyledon are exhausted; the cotyledon or cotyledon leaves wither and drop. At this stage, germination is completed, and the plant is considered a seedling. Once a seedling, the plant continues growth and development through juvenile and mature plant stages.

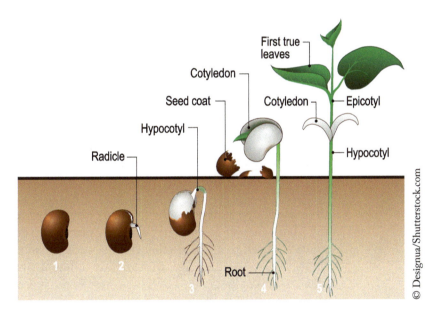

Seed Germination

- Beginning of life as growing from seeds
- Three conditions for proper germination
  - *Water (first process of germination)*
  - *Oxygen (cellular respiratory process)*
  - *Suitable temperature (average 70°F–80°F)*

- Radicle (primary root) to emerge

GERMINATION AND PLANT LIFE CYCLE

Lecture Contents (*continued*)

© MSSA/Shutterstock.com

Plant Life Cycle

Some species sprout from seed, flourish with foliage and flower, produce new seed, and die in one season. We call such species annuals. They're generally fast growing, because they go all the way through their life cycle in 1 year or less.

A biennial is a flowering plant that produces roots and foliage in the first year, then, after a period of dormancy, produces its flowers and fruit (seed) in the second year, and then die (e.g., *Foxglove*). A carrot is also a biennial; if left in the ground, it would produce flowers (and carrot seed) in its second year of growth.

A perennial is a flowering plant that lives on and on, and produces flowers each of its years. A rose is a perennial. You will see its flowers year after year. A monocarp is a flowering plant that lives on and on, but doesn't flower except once in its lifetime. A monocarp might go as many as 35 years without flowering. Then it flowers once, and is finished, and dies (an example is the century plant *Agave americana*).

Regardless of how long it lives, a plant will start pass through three more phases after germination, including juvenility, maturation, and senescence. Plants show different characteristics and have different functions at each stage, as described below:

In the juvenile stage, the plant will gain a great deal of vegetative growth (leaves, stems, roots), but won't yet produce its flowers. A plant may stay in the juvenile stage for days, months, or even years, depending on the species. The plants' appearance may be a bit different in its juvenile stage, with slightly different size and shape of leaf. Leaves are known to persist longer on a deciduous tree in the juvenile stage.

At maturation, the plant will produce flowers for reproduction. Flowers are produced in three stages: induction, initiation, and development. The first phase of induction can be caused by environmental factors of night length and cool temperatures. This phase is a chemical process going on inside the plant and it cannot be detected by the naked eye. The flower Initiation phase is next. It is detectable, but only at the microscopic level. Flower meristems begin to develop in this phase, as shown in the following figures. And finally, the flower development phase brings forth the opening of the flower, revealing the reproductive parts to pollination.

Senescence is defined as the condition or process of deterioration with age. All plants reach a point where they begin to deteriorate. Plants have a life span and expectancy. The life span can vary from several weeks to thousands of years.

GERMINATION AND PLANT LIFE CYCLE

Lecture Contents (*continued*)

Plant Life Cycle (*continued*)

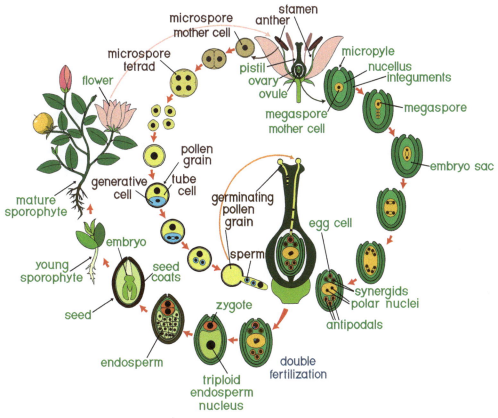

Life Cycle of Flowering Plant

© Kazakova Maryia/Shutterstock.com

GERMINATION AND PLANT LIFE CYCLE

Lecture Contents (*continued*)

Plant Life Cycle (*continued*)

Life Cycle of Pine Tree

© Kazakova Maryia/Shutterstock.com

GERMINATION AND PLANT LIFE CYCLE

Lecture Contents (*continued*)

Plant Life Cycle (*continued*)

Life Cycle of Fern

© Kazakova Maryia/Shutterstock.com

GERMINATION AND PLANT LIFE CYCLE

Lecture Contents (*continued*)

Plant Life Cycle (*continued*)

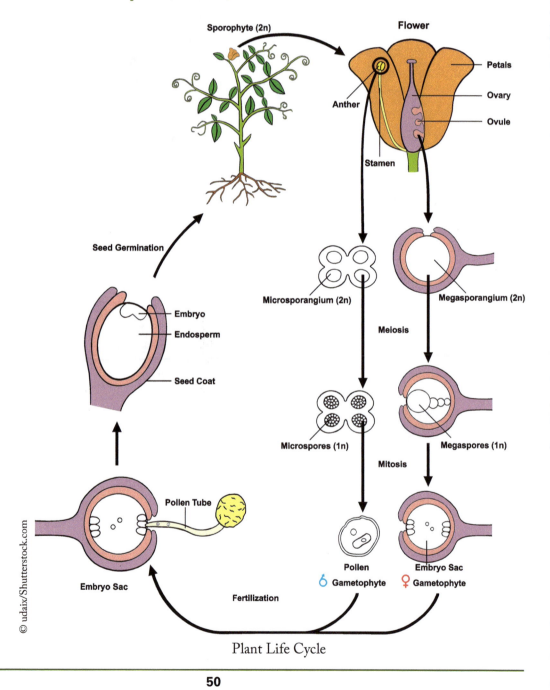

Plant Life Cycle

GERMINATION AND PLANT LIFE CYCLE

Relevant Links

TEDTalk
Scenes From the Millennium Seed Bank:
Q&A with Jonathan Drori   https://blog.ted.com/more_news_from/

Wiki (Reference purpose only)
Germination   https://en.wikipedia.org/wiki/Germination

CHAPTER 3

GERMINATION AND PLANT LIFE CYCLE

Quizzes

© Davidovka/Shutterstock.
com

1. Describe three primary conditions of proper seed germination.

2. _____ is the way to support seed germination by breaking hard coat of seed. Give three examples of doing that.

3. Describe the difference between *epigeous* germination and *hypogeous* one.

PLANT PHYSIOLOGY

Relevant Words

Autotroph, Cellular respiration, Photosynthesis, Physiology, Translocation, Transpiration

Lab Objective

To observe and to learn about plant's important actions for its germination and growth.

Lab Assignment

- Identify the optimum conditions of soil, water, and light for the plants sown during the last lab assignment experiment.
- Research about photosynthesis, transpiration, and cell respiration.
- Describe how these important actions affect the plant's growth.

Lecture Outlines

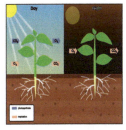

© Preeda340/Shutterstock.com

❖ Photosynthesis
❖ Transpiration
❖ Cellular Respiration
❖ Environment Stimulation

PLANT PHYSIOLOGY

Lecture Contents

Plant physiology is the study of how plants function. They produce their own energy. They move water and nutrients throughout their parts. They grow and respond to their environment. But how? Basic plant functions are discussed in this chapter.

Plant Metabolism

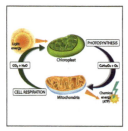

© Sakurra/Shutterstock.com

There are countless processes going on in a living plant at all times. Cells are dividing, stems are elongating and thickening. Flowers are produced. Strong scents are produced. Fruits are produced and ripened. All these life processes are achieved through a complicated series of metabolic chemical reactions, or metabolism.

Plant metabolism requires an influx of chemicals and energy to power these reactions. Plants acquire needed chemicals and water through soil moisture, and/or nutrients supplied by fertilizers. They acquire energy from the sun.

Photosynthesis

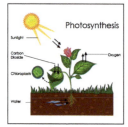

© Vecton/Shutterstock.com

Photosynthesis is Latin for "putting together with light." Water, carbon dioxide, light energy, and chlorophyll are its ingredients. A plant produces its own energy, and is therefore known as an *autotroph* ("self-nourishing"). Plants create energy in the form of carbohydrate (sugar) molecules. This enables the plants to "power" their metabolic life processes. This also creates energy for animals and humans that eat the plants, and provides energy for humans who eat the animals, which eat the plants, as well.

In the process of creating this energy, a green plant consumes carbon dioxide and liberates oxygen. Plants take in a potentially harmful greenhouse gas (CO_2), provide us with energy, and produce oxygen for us to breath. We would suggest, therefore, that this is indeed one of the most important chemical reactions on the planet. The phenomenon of photosynthesis is quite complex. But in simple terms, the process can be summarized by the following sequence:

The sun's energy is absorbed by the chlorophyll in the leaf (and/or in the stem of certain species). The sun's energy "excites" the molecules in the leaf. The hydrogen (H) then splits off the water molecule (H_2O). The H joins with the carbon dioxide (CO_2) molecule to form a carbohydrate ($C_6H_{12}O_6$) sugar molecule. The sugar molecules are transported throughout the plant via the phloem, and "freed-up" O_2 is released through the stomata. The chemical formula is **$6CO_2 + 6H_2O + Light\ Energy = C_6H_{12}O_6 + 6O_2$.**

PLANT PHYSIOLOGY

Lecture Contents (*continued*)

Photosynthesis (*continued*)

Freed-up O_2 is the oxygen we breathe. That is why plants are said to "clean the air." Actually, it might be said, plants "provide" fresh clean air. A human breathes about 740 kg of oxygen per year, which is, very roughly, seven or eight trees' worth of oxygen produced (http://www.sciencefocus.com/qa/how-many-trees-are-needed-provide-enough-oxygen-one-person).

Another very important part of this process is carbon dioxide consumption. Let's examine CO_2 a bit further:

A greenhouse gas is a gas, trapping the earth's heat, which contributes to the "*greenhouse effect*.". They let in most of the incoming solar radiation that heats the earth's surface yet prevent part of the outgoing thermal radiation from escaping to space. They are termed greenhouse gases because the layer of gas keeps the earth warm, like a greenhouse roof keeps a greenhouse warm. Water vapor is one such gas. Carbon dioxide, as stated above, is also a greenhouse gas (other gases contribute as well).

The greenhouse effect is a natural phenomenon that is absolutely critical for life on earth. Without the layer of natural gases, the earth would be too cold to grow food, as the average global temperature would be 0°F (or –18°C). This natural phenomenon works well for us, and even protects us, unless of course, the balance is askew.

Atmospheric carbon dioxide levels are of global concern however, because of two significant trends. First, we are taking plants out of the cycle at an alarming pace. Plants absorb CO_2 and convert it to energy. Imagine if plants covered the planet (as they once did). Surely so many plants could absorb an abundance of CO_2!

We are cutting down trees at a pace of 150 acres every minute every day. How many millions of trees are harvested for mail-order catalogs? It is estimated that the Amazon rainforest alone is vanishing at the rate of 20,000 sq. miles a year (from Rainforest Facts June 14, 2018 http://www.rain-tree.com/facts.htm). If there are less trees to consume the CO_2 through their leaves, where will the carbon dioxide go instead? It thickens the greenhouse roof over our heads and makes things warmer.

The second part of the problem is that we are burning more carbon. We are putting more carbon dioxide in the atmosphere at the same time that we are chopping down the ultimate remedy. More cars. More coal-fired energy plants, less trees. This is a problem.

Lecture Contents (*continued*)

Photosynthesis (*continued*)

Some argue that greenhouse gases fluctuate naturally over time, and they do. The planet has experienced ice age and interglacial conditions as well. But there is evidence that human activity is exacerbating this problem as we burn fossil fuels, clear forests, and use gasoline-dependent transportation. "The amount of carbon dioxide (CO_2) has increased by 30% since pre-industrial times (from about 270 molecules of CO_2 per million molecules of air in 1850 to the present 360 parts per million), and continues to rise over time, due primarily to the burning of fossil fuel" (https://www.giss.nasa.gov/research/briefs/ma_01/).

While the debate rages on, we are beginning to see dramatic effects of record heat and increasingly powerful storms. But even just a small change in the average global temperature has a major impact.

At the end of the last ice age, when the northeastern United States was covered by more than 3,000 ft of ice, average temperatures were only 5°F to 9°F cooler than today. During the Paleocene–Eocene Thermal Maximum 55 million years ago, when crocodiles and palm trees lived above the Arctic Circle, the average global temperature was only 8°F to 13°F warmer than today (http://www.climatesignals.org/data/record-high-temps-vs-record-low-temps).

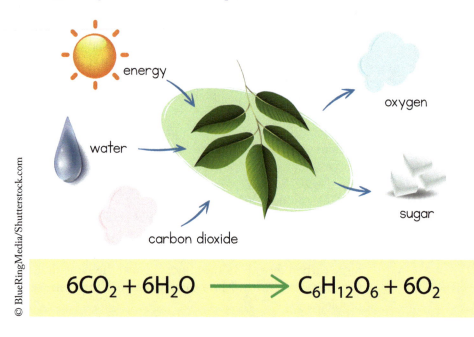

energy

water

carbon dioxide

oxygen

sugar

© BlueRingMedia/Shutterstock.com

$$6CO_2 + 6H_2O \longrightarrow C_6H_{12}O_6 + 6O_2$$

PLANT PHYSIOLOGY

Lecture Contents (*continued*)

Photosynthesis (*continued*)

© trgrowth/Shutterstock.com

- Plant process to convert light energy into chemical energy to fuel the plants' activities
- Stored in *carbohydrate* molecules, such as sugars, synthesized from *carbon dioxide* and water
- Oxygen released as a byproduct
- *Calvin cycle (light–independent reactions of photosynthesis)*
  - A metabolic process in the stroma of the chloroplast, converting CO_2 to the form of sugar
  - Carbon reactions pathway

Lecture Contents (*continued*)

Photosynthesis (*continued*)

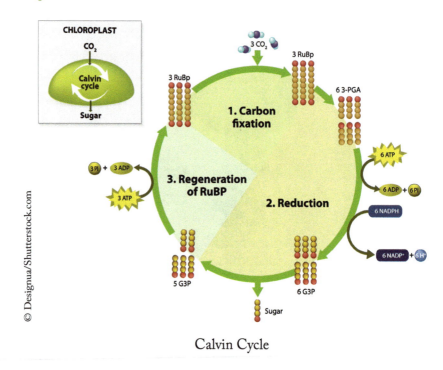

Calvin Cycle

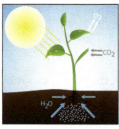

© wawritto/Shutterstock.com

Absorption

- Intakes of water and minerals
- Primary function of the roots
- *Foliar absorption*—Absorption through the leaves
  - Active absorption: Energy and oxygen required
  - Passive absorption: Osmosis (moving only water through cell membranes)

PLANT PHYSIOLOGY

Lecture Contents (*continued*)

Absorption (*continued*)

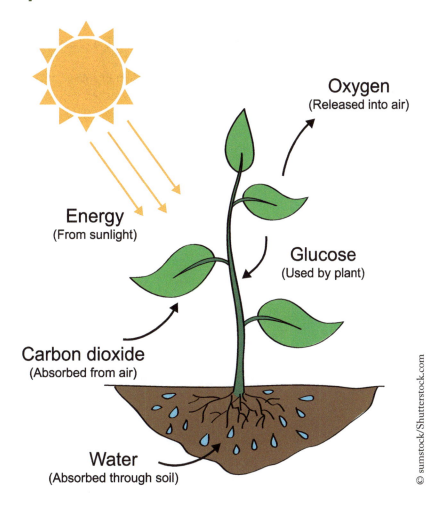

Oxygen
(Released into air)

Energy
(From sunlight)

Glucose
(Used by plant)

Carbon dioxide
(Absorbed from air)

Water
(Absorbed through soil)

© sumstock/Shutterstock.com

PLANT PHYSIOLOGY

Lecture Contents (*continued*)

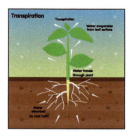

© Preeda340/Shutterstock.
com

Transpiration: Water Absorption and Transport

Water, as noted, is critical for photosynthesis and other plant functions. Transpiration is the means by which water moves through a plant via the xylem.

Molecules tend to cling together. When like molecules stick together, it is termed cohesion. When unlike molecules cling together, it is called adhesion. Both cohesion and adhesion are important forces in nature that work together to help absorb and transport water (and soluble nutrients) in a living plant.

As mentioned in Chapter 2, stomata are tiny openings in the underside of a leaf. When water molecules evaporate from the stomata, they tend to "pull" other water molecules along through cohesion. Other water molecules cling to the evaporating molecules to naturally replenish the gap. The loss of water and the constant replenishment thereof keep the cycle of transpiration going.

© Jakinnboaz/Shutterstock.com

PLANT PHYSIOLOGY

Lecture Contents *(continued)*

Transpiration: Water Absorption and Transport *(continued)*

"During a growing season, a leaf will transpire many times more water than its own weight. An acre of corn gives off about 3,000–4,000 gallons (11,400–15,100 liters) of water each day, and a large oak tree can transpire 40,000 gallons (151,000 liters) per year" (http://water.usgs.gov/edu/watercycletranspiration.html).

- Opposite of absorption—Loss of water from the plant
- Water vapor released from the leaves (stomata—guard cells), stems, flowers
- Water intake from absorption = water used in photosynthesis + water loss through transpiration
- Vital for the movement of minerals, keeping cool

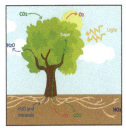

© Mari-Leaf/Shutterstock.com

Translocation

Translocation is the movement of sugar in a plant. The energy that is produced in the leaves must go to all parts of the plant to fuel its growth and development. The energy flows via the *phloem*.

The movement is made possible because of internal pressure created through osmosis. The movement of water through a semipermeable cell wall into a solution of concentrated sugar molecules inside the cell creates a great deal of internal pressure. The pressure causes sap to move through the phloem toward where the energy is needed. This pressure is "over ten times the pressure in an automobile tire" (http://www.biologyreference.com/Ta-Va/Translocation.html#ixzz5IhfomwFs).

- Movement of carbohydrates, minerals, and water through the plant
  - Xylem: Water and mineral movement
  - Phloem: Sugar (source-to-snik) movement
    - Roots
    - Flowers, fruits, leaves, and seeds
    - Meristems, root tips

PLANT PHYSIOLOGY

Lecture Contents (continued)

Translocation (continued)

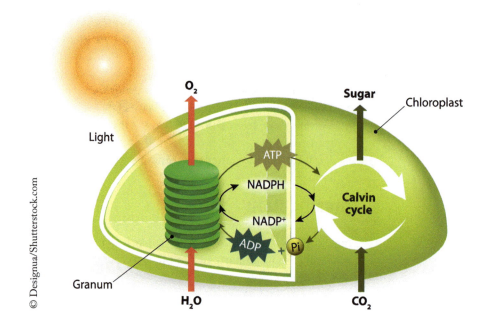

© Designua/Shutterstock.com

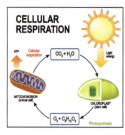

© Designua/Shutterstock.com

Cellular Respiration

Cellular respiration is essentially the opposite chemical reaction of photosynthesis. It is the utilization of the energy molecule that is created in photosynthesis; it is the "burning" of the carbohydrate produced. It is how plants get the energy they need to fuel metabolism. This is also how we get energy from the foods we eat. In this ("opposite") reaction, oxygen is consumed, and carbon dioxide is released. The chemical formula is as follows:

$$C_6H_{12}O_6 + 6\,O_2 \rightarrow 6\,CO_2 + 6\,H_2O$$

When we breathe in, we enable oxygen to facilitate burning carbohydrates (we need more air when we're burning carbs hard and fast). Then, with every breath we exhale, we are putting CO_2 in the air. Our body burns carbohydrate molecules to survive (even our sleeping heartbeat is powered in this way).

The same is true of plants. They need to break down the sugars they have created into energy. They utilize the O_2 resulting from photosynthesis to oxidize the energy molecules.

PLANT PHYSIOLOGY

Lecture Contents (*continued*)

Cellular Respiration (*continued*)

This releases the energy that is stored in the bonds. Plants also need energy at night, when there is no sunlight. Thus, plants must absorb oxygen from the air and give off carbon dioxide. Plants produce approximately 10 times more oxygen during the day than what they consume at night (http://scienceline.ucsb.edu/getkey.php?key=2860).

Anytime a carbon molecule is burned, CO_2 is released. Again, plants absorb CO_2. When a plant dies, it still contains this carbon. When we burn firewood, (which still is a primary source of heating and cooking in the developing world) we are releasing trapped carbon. When we burn the remnants of a cut rainforest, we certainly add injury to insult.

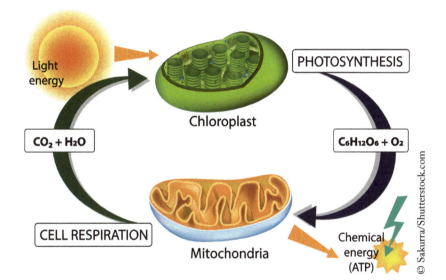

Imagine millions of years of dead plants covered in mud or sand. Then, carbon in those plants would be trapped and fossilized. Hence fossil fuels. Rich in energy molecules, indeed. We burn those energy molecules every day. We burn them with an increasing appetite. The majority of new automobiles are not getting better fuel economy at present; they're getting more powerful, by popular demand. We are burning energy molecules long held in plants (and animals), and are releasing megatons of carbon dioxide.

The burning of coal for energy also produces carbon dioxide, as coal is simply fossilized carbon. When we burn coal, we release increased carbon dioxide. Due to deforestation, there are less green plants to absorb this greenhouse gas. Still, we continue to burn more

PLANT PHYSIOLOGY

Lecture Contents (*continued*)

Cellular Respiration (*continued*)

coal. Hence the looming, potentially disastrous consequences of a natural system widely out of balance.

- Opposite reaction to photosynthesis
- Carbohydrate + Oxygen = Energy + Water + CO2
- Energy used for chlorophyll formation, flowers, fruits, absorption of water and nutrients
- *Citric acid cycle (Krebs cycle or tricarboxylic acid [TCA] cycle)*
  - Metabolic pathway of chemical reaction to generate energy through the oxidation of acetate

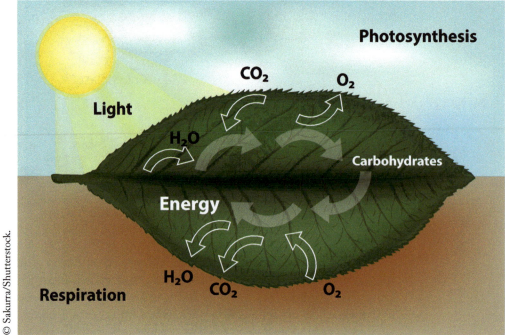

© Sakurra/Shutterstock.

<table>
<tr><td>CHAPTER 4</td><td></td></tr>
</table>

CHAPTER 4   PLANT PHYSIOLOGY

Relevant Links

TEDTalk
The Roots of Plant Intelligence   https://www.ted.com/talks/stefano_mancuso_the_roots_of_
plant_intelligence?utm_campaign=tedspread&utm_medium=
referral&utm_source=tedcomshare

Organization
American Society of Plant Biologists   https://aspb.org

Wiki (Reference purpose only)
Cellular Respiration   https://en.wikipedia.org/wiki/Cellular_respiration
Photosynthesis   https://en.wikipedia.org/wiki/Photosynthesis
Transpiration   https://en.wikipedia.org/wiki/Transpiration

Quizzes

© Davidovka/Shutterstock.
com

1. What is the chemical formula for photosynthesis?

2. The opposite action of photosynthesis is called _____, which provides for a release of the energy of the carbohydrate molecule created.

3. Describe briefly the "*Calvin cycle.*"

POLLINATION

Relevant Words

Abiotic, Anemophily, Anther, Biotic, Chiropterophily, Colony collapse disorder, Cross-pollination, Dioecious, Embryo, Entomophily, Gamete, Hydrophily, Monoecious, Ornithophily, Ovum, Self-pollination, Sperm, Stigma, Zoophily, Zygote

Lab Objective

To research and describe types of *pollination* identified from an observation at the local nursery.

Lab Assignment

- Visit a local nursery again and identify the different types of pollination from plants observed.
- Take photos or sketches and make notes of identified pollination methods.
- Describe briefly the different pollination method, comparing to other ways of pollination.

Lecture Outlines

© bsd/Shutterstock.com

❖ Pollination: Self Versus Cross
❖ Pollination Method: Anemophily, Chiropterophily, Entomophily, Hydrophily, Ornithophily, and Zoophily

POLLINATION

Lecture Contents

© Serbey Merkulov/
Shutterstock.com

Pollination

As in animals, reproduction in plants is a sexual process. The cell that is formed by the union of a male sex cell (sperm) and a female sex cell (ovum) is called a *zygote*. A zygote develops into an embryo. The unification of a sperm and an ovum to form a zygote constitutes sexual reproduction.

Each pollen grain in a flowering plant contains two cells. The first, a tube cell, produces a pollen tube that forms from stigma to ovary with amazing precision. The second is a reproductive cell (the male gamete). The gamete releases the sperm nuclei. The sperm nuclei flow through the pollen tube to an awaiting egg (the female gamete). When the sperm and egg(s) unite, fertilization occurs. The eggs become seeds, housed in an ovary. The ovary swells as the seeds mature and ripen (this we know as a fruit).

The needed pollen is produced and stored in a flower's anther. So, there must be a means of transferring pollen from the anther to the stigma, for this reproductive process to occur. The transfer of pollen from anther to stigma is called pollination.

Biotic pollination is a term applied to the movement and distribution of pollen by living things. There are quite a few living things acting as "agents" of biotic pollination. Included are movement by insects such as bees, butterflies, moths, flies, and beetles (entomophily); movement by birds (ornithophily); movement by bats (chiropterophily); and other animals such as monkeys, deer, rabbits, rodents, lizards, and bears (zoophily). Abiotic pollination is characterized as pollination via nonliving things such as wind (anemophily), and sometimes water (hydrophily).

The differences between flower structures of biotic versus abiotic pollinated flowers are numerous. Flowers take an enormous amount of energy for a plant to produce and maintain. Colorful parts, strong scents, and ample sweet sugary liquid are a drain on the plant, but, are important to attract pollinating insects. Of course, wind-pollinated flowering plants don't need to expand energy on large showy petals and sweet scents because they do not rely on attracting insects. The petals are generally small and brown or green instead.

Pollen is sticky and spiky on a biotic pollenated plant, so the pollen will adhere to insects for dispersal. It is smooth and light on an abiotic pollinated plant so that it blows in the wind without clumping. There is more quantity of pollen in the abiotic types because it doesn't always reach its target. Wind could be too strong, or not strong enough.

POLLINATION

Lecture Contents (*continued*)

Pollination (*continued*)

Differences include structure and placement of anthers and stigma; in the biotic species, the anther is firm, and the stigma is inside, so that an insect can brush against them. In the abiotic species, the anthers are loosely attached so they will shake in the wind to disperse pollen, and the stigma is feathery and net-like, on the outside of the flower, to catch pollen in the wind. Whichever mode of movement, when pollen is transferred from the anther of a flower to the stigma of the same flower, self-pollination is said to occur. When pollen is transferred from the anther of a flower to the stigma of a different flower (of the same species), cross-pollination is said to occur.

If pollination choices are limited, self-pollination can be an advantage. But cross-pollination is the desirable mode in nature, because it allows for DNA from different plants (of the same species) to be mixed. This serves to diversify the species. Diversity, in turn, strengthens the species. This is how adaptation and evolution work best. We referred to this in Chapter 3 with a discussion of *hybrid vigor*. Nature sets elaborate schemes to encourage cross-pollination. Often, a flower's stigma ripens at a different time than the anther, thus self-pollination is not possible. Female pine cones are located at the top of the tree, and male cones are at the bottom. Sometimes the male and female flowers are not even on the same plant, a characteristic known as a *dioecious* (when male and female flowers are on the same plant, the plant is said to be *monoecious*. Latin—one house).

Pollination is extremely important, and of course, not only for the survival of the plant, but for humans (and other animals) as well. One out of every three bites of food we eat depends on pollinators and the resultant pollination. Pollinators are needed on more than 1,200 different food crops globally, worth over $200 billion. Pollinators also support healthy ecosystems that clean the air, stabilize soils, protect from severe weather, and support other wildlife (http://pollinator.org/pollinators).

Meanwhile, pollinator populations worldwide are in decline. Loss of habitat, pesticides, pollution, and other toxic chemicals are to blame. Colony collapse disorder is causing bee populations to plummet. Add climate change to the equation, with flowers sometimes blooming early (before the arrival of required pollinators) or sometimes blooming late (after the departure of required pollinators), and we see the natural system again at risk. One must not underestimate the importance of creating and maintaining healthy habitat for pollinators. And one must not underestimate what pollinators do to maintain healthy ecosystems. Three out of four flowering plants depend on them. Pollinating insects are essential to ecosystem biodiversity.

POLLINATION

Lecture Contents (*continued*)

Pollination (*continued*)

The Xerces Society, of Portland Oregon, is a nonprofit environmental organization that focuses on the conservation of pollinating insects. It was named in honor of the extinct "Xerces blue" California butterfly. The society has launched a nationwide public outreach plan to foster increased awareness about the importance and plight of the pollinating insects. The project is called The Million Pollinator Garden Challenge. It is a call for action: a challenge to create and preserve a million pollinator gardens across the United States. Efforts like these must be implemented on a global basis.

What can we do to create pollinator habitat? It is quite simple. Provide food, shelter, and a habitat free of harmful chemicals.

For food, plant the right plants, and pollinators will come. They are drawn to a diversity of flowers, but pollinators and other beneficial insects seem to prefer easy landing pads. A spherical or flat-topped inflorescence (such as head, umbel, corymb, or cyme) seems especially well suited. They seek pollen and sugar-rich nectar as their food source, and they pick up and spread pollen from flower to flower as they gather it. Pollinators need this food source from early spring through late summer. So, it is important to plant flowing species that bloom early, bloom midseason, and bloom late season as well. The Natural Resource Conservation Service (NRCS), a department of the United States Department of Agriculture (USDA), is a valuable resource with respect to which plants are recommended as habitat in a particular part of the United States (https://plants.usda.gov/pollinators/NRCSdocuments.html). Native plant species are particularly valuable.

Providing shelter means preserving their nests. Soil is an important home for many species of bee and other important pollinator insects. There are 4,000 species of bee native to North America. Seventy percent of those species reside in the soil and rear their young there. Soil bees like it sunny and dry. It is thus recommended that a spot of soil be left bare, near or in the pollinator garden. Some species of bee travel only several hundred feet from their home (while bumble bees can travel up to 2 miles).

Wood-nesting bees are solitary, and often make individual nests in beetle tunnels left under the bark of a dead standing tree. If you're like others and your garden doesn't have a dead tree in it, a stump or chunk of wood with holes drilled in it would be helpful.

POLLINATION

Lecture Contents (*continued*)

Pollination (*continued*)

Bumble bees and other cavity-nesting bees make use of small spaces in abandoned rodent burrows and such.

Avoid the use of chemicals in the garden. There are so many chemicals that kill pollinators, and/or kill the food that they eat. It is in fact, what pesticides and herbicides do. They kill insects. And dandelions (*Taraxacum officinale*) are an important food source in early spring. It is best not to kill them with weed killers. In the best scenario, a garden and urban farm would be chemical free.

When that is not possible, it is absolutely critical that chemicals be used prudently. One must read the label and choose a narrow spectrum, that is, one that only targets a very small group of pests alone. Broad-spectrum insecticides kill hundreds of species or more, including beneficial insects and pollinators. Less toxic pest management strategies are discussed in Chapter 10, further in this text.

Plant Maturity

1. Flower induction
   - The first indication of maturity
   - Initial chemical reaction of flowering process
   - Environmental factors—Cool temperature (needed for *vernalization*: ability to flower), daily night duration (photoperiod: *phytochrome*—flowering pigment), intensity of light

2. Flower initiation
   - Phase of flowering invisible, taking place in the microscopic parts of the plant
   - Vegetative meristems changed to flower meristems (vegetative to reproductive)
   - Beginning of the flower parts development

3. Flower development
   - Opening of the flower as the final stage of development
   - Longer development period in cold climate

POLLINATION

Lecture Contents (*continued*)

Pollination (*continued*)

Plant Pollination

1. Self-pollination—Pollinating itself
2. Cross-pollination—Pollinated by another plant
   - ○ Pollens from the anthers deposited on the stigma by wind or insects
   - ○ Fertilization: Uniting of sperm in the pollen and eggs in the ovary
   - ○ Self-incompatibility: Unable to fertilize the eggs produced by the same flower (40% of cultivated plants)—cross-pollination is the solution

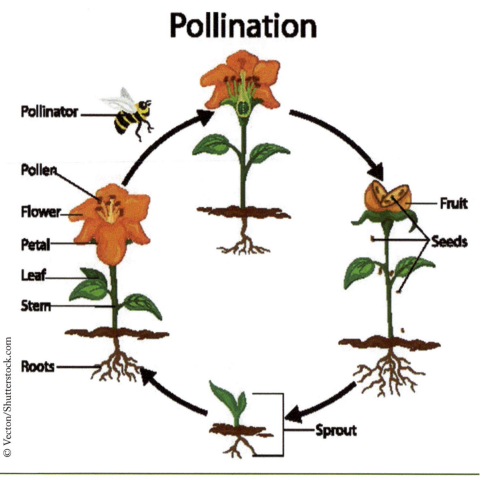

Lecture Contents (*continued*)

Pollination (*continued*)

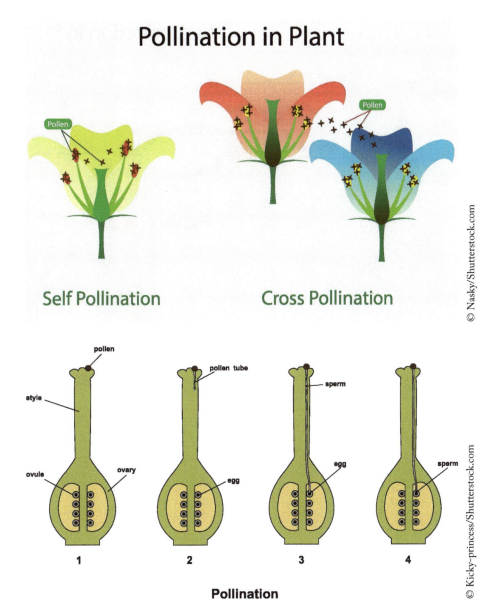

© Nasky/Shutterstock.com

© Kicky-princess/Shutterstock.com

POLLINATION

Lecture Contents (*continued*)

Pollination (*continued*)

Reproduction in Plants

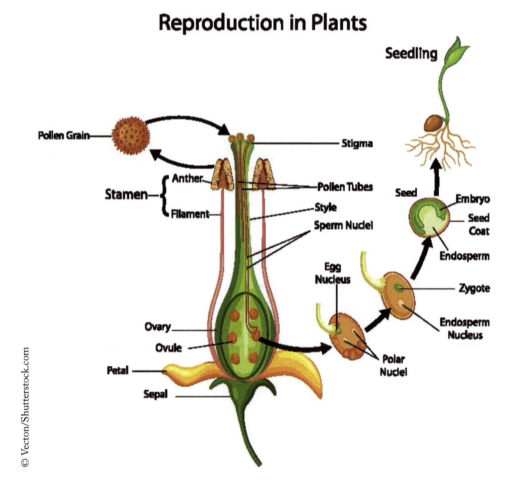

© Vecton/Shutterstock.com

POLLINATION

Relevant Links

TEDTalk

Every Pollen Grain Has a Story

https://www.ted.com/talks/jonathan_drori_every_pollen_grain_has_a_stor

The Beautiful Tricks of Flowers

https://www.ted.com/talks/jonathan_drori_the_beautiful_tricks_of_flowers

The Hidden Beauty of Pollination

https://www.ted.com/talks/louie_schwartzberg_the_hidden_beauty_of_pollination

Wiki (Reference purpose only)

Colony Collapse Disorder   https://en.wikipedia.org/wiki/Colony_collapse_disorder

Pollination   https://en.wikipedia.org/wiki/Pollination

Zygote   https://en.wikipedia.org/wiki/Zygote

POLLINATION

Quizzes

1. Describe briefly the difference between self-pollination and cross-pollination.

2. Movement and distribution of pollen by living things is called _____, on the contrary, one by nonliving things is called _____.

3. What is colony collapse disorder? And, what is the primary cause of it?

PROPAGATION

Relevant Words

Air layering, Approach graft, Bulb blindness, Cleft graft, Cloning, Cutting, Division, Genes, Grafting, Hardwood cutting, Leaf cutting, Propagation, Propagule, Rhizomes, Root cutting, Semi-hardwood cutting, Softwood cutting, Splicing, Stem cutting, Stolon, T-budding, Whip graft

Lab Objective

To research and describe propagation method that may be best suited for a specific plant selected.

Lab Assignment

- Research the propagation method that may be most suitable for your favorite plants selected.
- Describe daily conditions of the plant environment—Lighting hours, water frequency, and other elements supporting its propagation.
- Observe plant growth rate—The current height of plants.

Lecture Outlines

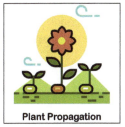

Plant Propagation

© Chanut Wongrattana/
Shutterstock.com

❖ Vegetative (Asexual) Propagation From Parts of Existing Plants (Cloning)
❖ Budding and Grafting

PROPAGATION

Lecture Contents

© Morphart Creation/
Shutterstock.com

Propagation

We have discussed seeds, cross-pollination, genetics and phenomenon of hybrid vigor, which have made plants healthier, sweeter, tastier, and, being able to withstand environmental threats and long distance shipping. Horticulturalists have been busy improving plants and plant traits for thousands of years.

When we cross plants via pollination in search of "new and improved," we plan for best results, but we can't guarantee 100% uniformity. We have learned that genes (traits) are passed on from parent plant to offspring. There will be some variation, depending on the dominant or recessive traits involved.

Vegetative propagation differs in that 100% uniformity is achieved by the establishment of clones. Cloning is a process of creating a new organism (plant) from an existing. Each clone bears the same set of genetic instructions (genes) in the nucleus of every cell. One is able to lock in desirable traits, and lock in hybrid superiority. And the process is fast, inexpensive, and easy. In this chapter, we discuss various methods of creating new plants from existing plant parts, including leaf, stem, root cuttings, and grafts.

Division is a method of propagation wherein a new plant is simply separated from the parent plant by hand, knife, saw, and/or sharp spade. One gathers a whole section of the plant in division, including leaf, stem, and root, and the new pieces are replanted. It is one of the easiest methods of vegetative propagation because the "new" plants already have roots. Division works best with clump-forming perennials like ornamental bunch grasses, asparagus, blackberries, and herbaceous houseplants such as Boston fern (*Nephrolepis exaltata*) and Cast iron plant (*Aspidistra elatior*).

Succulents that form offsets are propagated by division. Some are simple and can be pulled apart by hand (*Sedum spp.*). Others such as *Sansevieria* have tough rhizomes and must sometimes be separated by small hand saw. Bamboo rhizomes are so strong they can easily split a ceramic container when too crowded, making the need for division obvious.

Bulbs are also propagated by division. They should be divided and replanted every 2 to 3 years to prevent overcrowding and congestion, which leads to "bulb blindness," a condition of diminished blooms; fewer and smaller, or no blooms at all. The optimal time for division is spring, when plants are in an active growth mode. If the plant is in a container, it must be removed. The plant is then divided and immediately replanted.

PROPAGATION

Lecture Contents (*continued*)

Propagation (*continued*)

Cuttings are taken from root, leaf, or stem. Choosing the correct method requires research, as needs vary by species. What method have horticulturalists used previously? Scientific curiosity, and a bit of trial and error also work well.

A **root cutting** is usually "taken" in winter or early spring before new growth appears on the plant. A 2 in. piece of root, about 1/8-in. thick is all that is required. Keep the cutting moist and cool, but not soaked. To mimic nature, it should be covered, as well. Plants that are commonly done by root cuttings include blanket flower (*Gaillardia*), Sage (*Salvia spp.*), and oriental poppy (*Papaver orientale*).

A **leaf cutting** is a cutting taken from leaf. The leaf must be thick and leathery, or thick and succulent, as it must be resistant to wilt during the development stage of its new adventitious roots. An entire leaf or just a portion thereof can be used for this method.

Devils tongue (*Sansevieria spp.*) was mentioned earlier as being propagated through division. It is also one that can be propagated by leaf cutting. Devil's tongue has long leaves measuring up to 3 to 4 ft depending on the species. A dozen or more cuttings can be taken from a single leaf. It is important to keep the root end of the leaf as the downward end when the propagule is stuck. A 3 in. piece of leaf is dipped in rooting hormone and stuck in the soilless potting media. Adventitious roots start to appear after 90 to 120 days, and a new *Sansevieria* is formed. If several rooted cuttings are placed in a container together, a fuller houseplant will be achieved in a significantly shortened time frame.

Other species that are commonly propagated by leaf cuttings include African violet (*Saintpaulia*), painted-leaf begonia (*Begonia rex*), and ripple peperomia (*Peperomia caperata*). Carefully slice a leaf at its midrib and apply a small amount of rooting hormone to the underside of the ¼-in. to ½-in. cut.

Most horticulturalists would probably recommend **stem cutting** as the desired method of vegetative propagation. Success can be achieved with relative ease, depending on the species selected. Stem cutting, as the name implies, involves taking a cutting from stem. Three-in. sections are cut, dipped in rooting hormone if needed, and stuck in the potting media.

PROPAGATION

Lecture Contents (continued)

Propagation (continued)

Cuttings of herbaceous (non-woody) stems, can be taken at any time of year. Woody stems, on the other hand, must be taken during an appropriate season (and development stage) depending again, on the particular species involved.

Some species are best propagated by **softwood cuttings**. A softwood cutting must be taken in spring, from the current season's new growth. Lilac (*Syringa vulgaris*) and Weigela (*Weigela spp.*) are two shrubs propagated via softwood cuttings.

Some species are best propagated by **semi-hardwood cuttings**. Semi-hardwood cuttings are taken in summer, from the maturing stems of current season growth. Ceanothus (*Ceanothus spp.*) and passion flower (*Passiflora*) are examples of species propagated by semi-hardwood cuttings.

A **hardwood cutting** is taken during fall through winter, when the plant is in its dormancy. Because of the need for dormancy, this method is mostly restricted to deciduous plants, and the ideal time is just after leaf fall. It also takes a full year for most species to develop roots with this method, so patience is required.

Hardwood cuttings will need to remain cool but protected over winter, as in an unheated greenhouse. Success requires excellent drainage, yet consistent moisture. A sandy garden loam works well. Insert 12-in. cuttings into the ground or pot. Leave 4 in. above grade. Blueberry (*Vaccinium spp.*), dogwood (*Cornus spp.*), honeysuckle (*Lonicera spp.*), grape (*Vitis spp.*), and rose (*Rosa spp.*) are examples of plants propagated via hardwood cuttings.

In certain species, adventitious roots may form when the plant's stems come into contact with the soil. A strawberry does this naturally. It grows horizontal stems called stolon. They bend toward the soil under their own weight. With moisture, new roots form and flowers will set. This is also evident in nature when a shrub is pinned by fallen tree. The stems in contact with the soil create roots and the plant is propagated vegetatively.

Horticulturalists mimic nature in the garden, greenhouse, or lab, by forcing a flexible stem into contact with moist soil. It can be pinned in place with a hook fashioned out of coat hanger or pinned with a rock. Plants propagated in this fashion include the climbing roses (*Rosa spp.*), Forsythia (*Forsythia spp.*), and wax myrtle (*Morella cerifera*).

PROPAGATION

Lecture Contents (*continued*)

Propagation (*continued*)

Sometimes we seek to induce layering along the stem, as described earlier, yet the branches are not flexible enough to bend the stems to the soil or potting media. In such case, a horticulturalist will employ a method known as air layering.

Air layering involves making a wound on the stem with a sharp knife, applying rooting hormone, covering the wound with moist sphagnum moss, and sealing it in a plastic "cocoon." The size and type of wound is important. With monocots, one must make an upward slice about one-third of the way into the stem with a width of 1-in. Secure the wound in an open position with a horizontal toothpick or wooded match stick. We then cover the wound with moist sphagnum peat moss several inches thick, and seal it from the elements with a covering of plastic, cinched tight at both ends.

The process for dicots involves cutting and removing a ring of bark all the way around the stem, just into the slippery cambium layer. The cut should be as tall as the stem is wide. A small amount of rooting hormone is applied to the wound. It is covered and secured with moist sphagnum and plastic, as described earlier. Plants propagated by air layering include rubber tree (*Ficus elastica*), Rhododendron (*Rhododendron spp.*), holly (*Ilex spp.*), and Magnolia (*Magnolia spp.*).

Both **grafting** and **T-budding** are forms of "splicing." We add a stem (or bud) from a species of the plant with a desirable trait onto a stem (or trunk) of a species with proven vigor and reliability. This is the case with the source of a favorite summer drink—pink lemonade.

A citrus grower had grown Eureka lemons for many years. The leaves of a Eureka lemon (*Citrus limon* 'Eureka') are solid green, the flowers white and the fruit lemon-yellow. On one sunny morning, the grower noticed an unusual new plant in the orchard. It had variegated leaves, pink flowers, and a pink tinged fruit. This was quite different. The grower tasted the fruit and found it to be especially sweet. A unique mutation was revealed. It was named a pink lemonade tree.

The grower planted the seeds of this tree, hoping for more of the diverse and tasty variation. The result was a reversion, however, to the original type Eureka lemons of yellow fruit and solid green leaves. This, of course we know, was due to the dominance of the yellow fruit gene. To establish a tree with 100% uniformity of this pink lemonade variation, the grower would need to employ the tactic of **grafting**.

PROPAGATION

Lecture Contents (*continued*)

Propagation (*continued*)

Grafting involves the splicing of one plant onto the stems or root stock of an existing healthy plant. When the wound heals successfully, the new trait is introduced onto the plant and is proliferated. Hybrid superiority and desirable traits are locked in.

With this method, stems of the variant pink lemonade tree are cut and removed. The slender trunk of a standard Eureka lemon is cut. A piece of pink lemon stem is spliced onto the trunk of the standard Eureka lemon. When the wound is healed, you have propagated a pink lemonade tree (*Citrus limon "Eureka Variegated Pink"*). Pink lemons will grow from the root of the Eureka lemon tree.

When the desirable trait (scion) is the same diameter of the root (root stock), the graft technique is known as a whip graft. When the scion is smaller than that of the root stock, the technique is known as a cleft graft. When the graft is from a fully rooted plant to the side of the plant being grafted, the technique is known as an approach graft. Whichever method employed, it is imperative that the "plumbing" (the xylem and phloem) is lined up between the scion and root stock, so the flow of its life energy (the sugars), water, and nutrients will continue.

T-budding is a form of grafting, except we are not grafting a stem onto stem or root stock. Instead, horticulturalists splice a bud from a plant with the desirable characteristics onto a plant with reliable, hardy roots and stems. It is named T-budding because of the shape of the cut made into the stem of the chosen root stock. A bud from the plant with desirable traits is inserted into the "T" slot. Grafting tape is applied until new growth emerges.

There are many variations on these techniques. Different species have unique characteristics that require a horticulturalist to be keen with his or her skills. Some plants propagate with relative ease like cutting the stem of a houseplant and placing it in a vase of water. Roots often quickly appear.

Horticulturalists use plant cloning to create hybrid strains of fruit, vegetables, and ornamental plants with locked-in hybrid superiority. High-yielding varieties with increased disease resistance and plant hardiness are reproduced with 100% uniformity. Such

Lecture Contents (*continued*)

Propagation (*continued*)

uniformity is not without problems however. Clones may have increased resistance to disease or environmental malady, but if one is diseased they are all diseased. Ecologically balanced natural systems, on the other hand, are rich in biodiversity.

This reduces susceptibility to one major disease that could devastate a whole species. While major improvements in food and medicines have been made through vegetative propagation methods, the importance of biodiversity in healthy ecosystems must be fully appreciated and managed with care.

Propagation Type

- Sexual propagation—Male and female cells join, and seeds are produced. *(Refer to Chapter 3 for more details.)*
  - Self-pollination (fertilizing itself)
  - Cross-pollination (fertilized by others)

    Hybrids: Offspring from cross-pollination (*hybrid vigor*—healthier, faster growing plants from selected hybrid seeds)

- Asexual (vegetative) propagation—Through parts of existing plants (daughter plants identically same as mother plants: exact genetic duplicates—*clones*)
  - Division: Rhizomes, tubers, stolons, crowns, offsets
  - Cutting: Root, stem, leaf, leaf-bud
  - Separation: Corms, bulbs
  - Layering: Tip, mound (stool), simple, air
  - Grafting: Whip, root, cleft, bark, bridge
  - Budding: Chip, patch, T-, ring

- Genetic makeup—The crossing of the two genetically pure lines of male and female
- Seeds from hybrid plants do not produce the same superior plants as the first generation for the second one.

Lecture Contents (*continued*)

Propagation (*continued*)

Reproduction in Plants

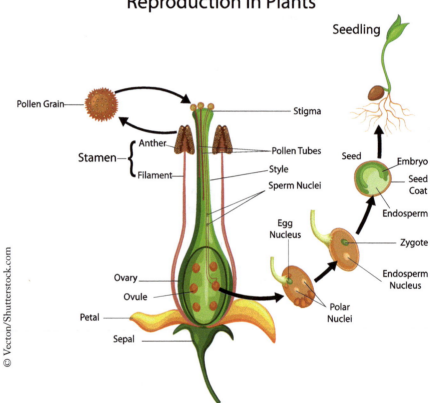

© Vecton/Shutterstock.com

Mendelian Genetics (*Refer to Chapter 3 for more details.*)

- *Gregor Mendel* to observe a series of plant breeding experiments—Height, color, flower position, seed color, seed shape, pod color, pod shape
  - *Phenotype*: The manifesting of the traits in a visible way
  - *Genotype*: The actual hereditary contents of offspring

- *Genes*—Traits in pairs in each parent (either recessive or dominant)
  - *Homozygous*: Same genes from both parents
  - *Heterozygous*: One gene from each parent

Lecture Contents (*continued*)

Propagation (*continued*)

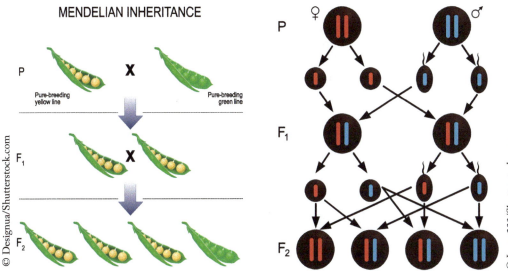

MENDELIAN INHERITANCE

P — Pure-breeding yellow line X Pure-breeding green line

© Designua/Shutterstock.com

© Lesya333/Shutterstock.com

Direct Seeding (*Refer to Chapter 3 for more details.*)

- Sowing seed outdoors
- Soil—Loose and crumble up to 1 ft per rocks or debris to be removed/free of clods
- Maintaining adequate soil moisture—Avoiding soil crusting

Indoor Seeding (*Refer to Chapter 3 for more details.*)

- Vegetables, flowers, and herbs
- Growing medium—Fast draining/nonpacking/to be sterilized (at 160°F–180°F) to avoid *damping-off* disease by fungi
- Sprinkling or misting for watering
- For rapid germination, 70°F to 80°F to be kept
- Transplanting after being crowd from germination—Watering after that (2–3 days in shaded area)
- Hardening-off before transplanting outside
- Transplanting outdoor in late afternoon—Watering after that

Lecture Contents (*continued*)

Propagation (*continued*)

Growing From Spores (*Refer to Chapter 3 for more details.*)

- Ferns
- *Prothallus*—Plant grown from spore drops, developing the sperm and egg
- Spore cases—On the undersides of the fronds
- Spore growing requirements—Warm, moist, air, and a growing medium

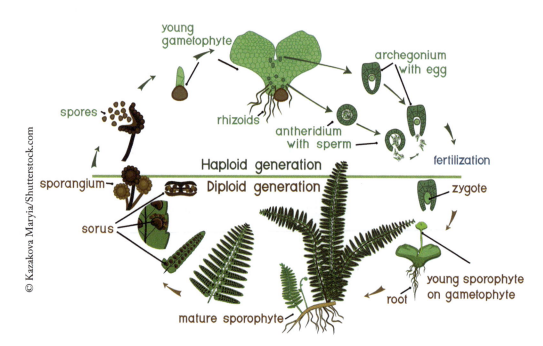

Vegetative Propagation

1. Cuttings: Regenerative parts cut from parent (stock) plants

   - Outdoor plant cutting
     - Superior rooting medium (two parts of sand, one part of peat moss, ine part of perlite, one part of vermiculite, pure vermiculite, pure perlite, and pure sand)
     - Hardwood cutting

PROPAGATION

Lecture Contents (*continued*)

Propagation (*continued*)

- Semi-hardwood cutting
- Softwood cutting
- Herbaceous cutting
- Root cutting

○ Indoor plant cutting
- Stem tip cutting
- Leaf bud cutting
- Stem section (cane) cutting
- Leaf cutting

2. Division/Separation
- Division and Separation are interchangeable
- Most common and reliable propagation method
- Dormant plants preferred

3. Layering
- Air layering
- Simple layering
- Tip layering
- Serpentine layering
- Trench layering
- Mound (stool) layering

4. Grafting
- Repair of girdled plants/creating unusual plants/changeover of fruit plants
- *Slippage*—Barks to be separated easily from the underlying woods

Three rules of grafting
- Rootstock diameter equal or larger than scion (pencil thickness)
- Cambium of the stock and scion in contact over a large area
- Stock and scion to fit tightly together, and, the joint to be protected from drying

PROPAGATION

Lecture Contents (*continued*)

Propagation (*continued*)

5. Budding
   - Patch of bark with a bud from a scion laying directly against the cambium of the stock
   - Less risky than grafting
   - Area of the union to be protected from drying with rubber ties

Tree grafting

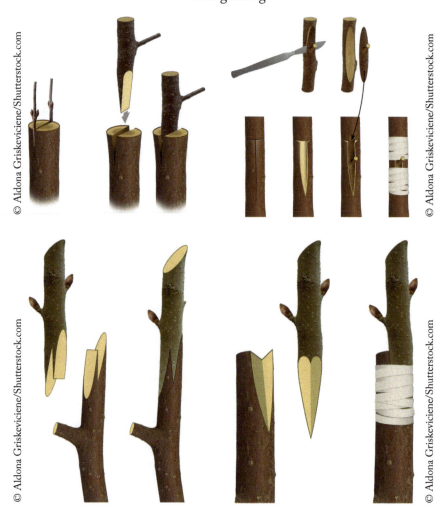

© Aldona Griskeviciene/Shutterstock.com

PROPAGATION

Relevant Links

TEDxBrainport
Indoor Farming, Plant Paradise   https://www.youtube.com/watch?v=ILzWmw53Wwo

Plant Propagation
Plant Propagation   http://plantpropagation.com

UC Master Gardener Napa County
Plant Propagation   http://ucanr.edu/sites/ucmgnapa/files/81929.pdf

Wiki (Reference purpose only)
Plant Propagation   https://en.wikipedia.org/wiki/Plant_propagation

PROPAGATION

Quizzes

© Davidovka/Shutterstock.
com

1. List three examples of asexual (vegetative) propagation, and, describe them briefly.

2. Name three advantages of vegetative propagation.

3. What are three types of grafts?

GENETICALLY MODIFIED ORGANISM

Relevant Words

Charles Darwin, Clustered Regularly Interspaced Short Palindromic Repeats (CRISPR), Genetic code, Genetically Modified Organism (GMO), Glyphosate, Herbert Boyer, Stanley Norman Cohen

Lab Objective

To research and identify genetically modified seeds sold in a local nursery, and compare them to organic seeds to find out the benefits of using non-genetically modified organism (GMO) ones, if any.

Lab Assignment

- Visit a local nursery.
- Identify three seed packages that are genetically modified.
- Research whether you can find natural organic seeds for three seed packages identified.
- If not being able to find, research the origin of seeds where they come from.
- Assess pros and cons of genetically modified seeds.
- Describe your personal belief about GMO.

Lecture Outlines

© Christos Georghiou/
Shutterstock.com

❖ Plant Genetics
❖ GMO and Biotechnology
❖ Impact on Natural Environment

GENETICALLY MODIFIED ORGANISM

Lecture Contents

© Vector Tradition/
Shutterstock.com

Genetically Modified Organism (GMO)

GMOs are making the headlines it seems, on an almost daily basis. Arguments are heard for and against. Meanwhile, horticulturalists have been cultivating improvements to plants for thousands of years. What is stirring the current controversy? The use of GMOs is both wide spread and restricted. Genetically modified plants are grown and cultivated in 26 countries. But, they are banned in 38 countries, including Germany, France, and Russia (https://gmo.geneticliteracyproject.org/FAQ/where-are-gmos-grown-and-banned/).

GMOs are organisms that have had their genetic material altered. Their genes have been edited by technology. As we discussed in Chapter 3, genes are the blueprints of an organism—the instructions for its life. Are we to mess with the integrity of natural systems in such a manner? Some think that we absolutely should not. Others say there is no worry.

Understanding Natural Selection and the Survival of the Fittest

Natural selection is defined as "a natural process that results in the survival and reproductive success of individuals or groups best adjusted to their environment and that leads to the perpetuation of genetic qualities best suited to that particular environment" (https://www.merriam-webster.com/dictionary/natural%20selection).

Organisms that are better adapted to their environment tend to survive and produce more offspring. This was the basis of Charles Darwin's work and his contribution to science and modern biology. It is key to his theory of evolution wherein a change in the heritable characteristics of an organism takes place over successive generations.

Charles Darwin (February 12, 1809 to April 19, 1882) was an English naturalist, geologist, and biologist. His interest in studying the change in hereditary traits overtime gave rise to the "family tree"; a diagram showing the history of the evolutionary relationships of a group of plants or animals.

Darwin's interests were not just limited to natural selection, but to artificial selection as well. Artificial selection is defined as the breeding of plants and animals to produce desirable traits. Humans have dealt with artificial selection for 12,000 years.

Some wolves (*Canis lupus*), for example, were observed early on, with a gentler demeanor. They appeared less wild and were perceived as less dangerous. Long ago, they were bred

GENETICALLY MODIFIED ORGANISM

Lecture Contents (*continued*)

Genetically Modified Organism (*continued*)

with other wolves that had a mild side as well, and dogs (*Canis spp.*) were domesticated over generations, as a result. Some were bred with short legs to help hunt rabbits. Some were bred to become poodles. It took generation after generation to succeed with the changes that occurred in the canines. Now they've become service dogs, rescue dogs, therapy dogs, and so on, and are regarded today as "man's best friend." These changes in inheritable traits over time were human induced and not natural.

If genes are molecules of instruction and blueprint, imagine for a minute, if we could artificially change those instructions. What if we could edit the genetic code? Any such attempt would need to be well thought out, of course, because these changes (or edits) would be passed on to future descendants of the altered organism as well.

What if we could cure a disease by altering the instructions of the disease carrying organism? With genetic editing biotechnology of today, we can. And we can do it with seeming precision.

Dr. Stanley Norman Cohen (born February 17, 1935) is an American geneticist. He partnered with biotech scientist Dr. Herbert Boyer in 1972. They are credited with being the first to successfully transplant genes from one living organism to another. Their work with *Escherichia coli* and Staphylococcus bacteria led to groundbreaking discoveries in the field of genetic engineering.

Studies by others included attempts to alter the genes of mosquitos. What if mosquitos were altered so they would be resistant (and therefore no longer carry and transmit) pathogens that cause malaria—a disease that kills 2,000,000 annually, including 1,000 children a day. Surely, such research is warranted.

In the 1980s, microbacteria were called to ecosystem rescue. They were genetically altered so they could digest oil in an oil spill.

1994 marked the first food being genetically modified. It was a tomato that had been altered for increased shelf life. A fruit must eventually rot in order to release and disperse its seeds. The tomato had been altered to suppress its rotting mechanism. Some say this is a major breakthrough for "food security."

GENETICALLY MODIFIED ORGANISM

Lecture Contents (*continued*)

Genetically Modified Organism (*continued*)

What if the genome of a plant could be altered to allow for increased drought or flood resiliency in the face of pending climate change? What if a tree could be altered to sequester carbon dioxide?

All trees absorb carbon, but none like the American chestnut (*Castanea dentate*) that once dominated eastern hardwood forests. There were an estimated three to four billion chestnut trees across more than 30 million acres. They grew fast, acquiring heights of a 10-story building and a trunk diameter of 12 ft. A study by Purdue University found them to store more carbon, and at a faster rate, than any other hardwood (https://www.americanforests.org/magazine/article/revival-of-the-american-chestnut/).

Sadly, the American chestnut was all but wiped out 100 years ago by the "chestnut blight." The blight has been called "the greatest ecological disaster to strike the world's forests in all of history" (https://www.acf.org/the-american-chestnut/history-american-chestnut/). But there is hope for a revival of these monarchs of the forest through genetic engineering. Researchers are attempting to produce an American chestnut with the addition of a few genes that confer disease resistance. (https://www.americanforests.org/magazine/article/revival-of-the-american-chestnut/).

The $11 million papaya industry was saved in Hawaii with genetic modification to the fruit so that it would be resistant to the papaya ringspot virus. Eggplant, a major food source in Bangladesh, was restored through genetic engineering. Rice has been genetically altered in the Philippines to add beta-carotene, the source of vitamin A, in a fight against malnourishment in poor countries.

The examples cited earlier seem to suggest research into genetic alteration is warranted. Still other examples spark protest.

Monsanto was an American chemical and bioengineering company founded in 1901 (it is now owned by Bayer AG of Leverkusen, Germany). Their primary products early on were pesticides and herbicides. They invented *glyphosate*, a broad-spectrum systemic herbicide (a weed killer commonly known as *Roundup*).

"The world is awash in glyphosate." A study published in the journal *Environmental Sciences Europe* reveals that Americans have applied 1.8 million tons of glyphosate

GENETICALLY MODIFIED ORGANISM

Lecture Contents (*continued*)

Genetically Modified Organism (*continued*)

since its introduction in 1974. Worldwide, 9.4 million tons of the chemical have been sprayed onto fields, which is equivalent to more than 2,300 Olympic-size swimming pools full.

It's also enough to spray nearly half a pound of Roundup on every cultivated acre of land in the world. Monsanto makes nearly $5 billion annually from sales of glyphosate worldwide (http://www.newsweek.com/glyphosate-now-most-used-agricultural-chemical-ever-422419).

Monsanto also discovered a gene in corn that, if genetically modified, would be resistant to their weed killer glyphosate. Imagine how much more herbicide they could sell, if the "desired" crops were resistant; an entire field could be sprayed repeatedly, without damage to the desired corn. Monsanto modified soybean and cotton to withstand glyphosate as well. They then patented the altered seed. If a farmer wants to spray weed killer, they have to buy the seed from Monsanto (Bayer) as well. Today, the majority of Monsanto's $14.6 billion in annual sales comes from their bioengineering and seeds divisions.

Another corporation (ArborGen Inc.) is hoping for approval to market a genetically engineered eucalyptus tree (*Eucalyptus spp.*) with increased frost hardiness. This would expand the company's lumber growing market. The tree, however, is not a native tree in North America and is even considered invasive in some regions. The tree is flammable and a drain on water resources in the arid Southwest. Environmentalists shudder at the thought.

Non-browning GMO apples are making their way to market. Like the earlier mentioned tomato, these fruits are engineered for longer shelf life. They will be sold sliced and packaged in plastic, for "ease and convenience" of lunch box preparation. Some hope this makes more kids eat apples. But still, millions of consumers worldwide are willing to pay extra, and insist upon non-GMO food.

Many say genetic engineering and the editing of genes is high-tech progress. Many think scientists are disrupting the Creator's instructions and blueprint, and often ponder a world with designer babies not too far off. Whatever your position on the issue, be aware that gene editing biotechnology is here to stay.

The latest genome editing technology is named *Clustered Regularly Interspaced Short Palindromic Repeats (CRISPR)*. It is named after a virus fighting mechanism discovered in bacteria. This new technology is to DNA processing, as Global Positioning System

GENETICALLY MODIFIED ORGANISM

Lecture Contents (*continued*)

Genetically Modified Organism (*continued*)

(GPS) devices are to maps. It is a total breakthrough. Discovered in 2012, *CRISPR* is a tool that edits a genome very precisely, very quickly, and at a fraction of the cost of earlier biotechnology.

CRISPR technology can be programmed to target specific stretches of genetic code and to edit DNA at precise locations. It is a system of "cut and paste," likened to a word processor for genes. With this technology, researchers can permanently modify genes in living cells and organisms and, in the future, may make it possible to correct mutations at precise locations in an organism's genome in order to treat genetic causes of disease (https://www.broadinstitute.org/what-broad/areas-focus/project-spotlight/questions-and-answers-about-crispr).

Featherless GMO chickens are easier to harvest. GMO salmon are faster growing. We can change genetic attributes and instructions now with relative ease. Will we discover radical improvements to human health? Or, are we opening a door that we can never close? Welcome, horticulturalists, to a whole new era.

GENETICALLY MODIFIED ORGANISM

Lecture Contents *(continued)*

Genetically Modified Organism *(continued)*

© Macrovector/Shutterstock.com

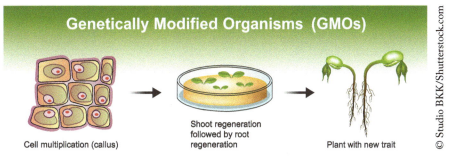

© Studio BKK/Shutterstock.com

GENETICALLY MODIFIED ORGANISM

Relevant Links

TEDTalk
The Case for Engineering Our Food

https://www.ted.com/talks/pamela_ronald_the_case_for_engineering_our_food

This Computer Will Grow Your
Food in the Future

https://www.ted.com/talks/caleb_harper_this_computer_ will_grow_your_food_in_the_future

Wiki (Reference purpose only)
Genetically Modified Organism

https://en.wikipedia.org/wiki/Genetically_modified_organism

GENETICALLY MODIFIED ORGANISM

CHAPTER 7

GENETICALLY MODIFIED ORGANISM

Quizzes

© Davidovka/Shutterstock.com

1. What does GMO stand for? And, identify three examples of GMO products.

2. What is the latest genetically modified organism (GMO) technology? And, describe it briefly.

3. What is the most commonly used genetically modified organism (GMO)-based chemical for the weed control?

SUSTAINABLE HORTICULTURE

SOIL AND COMPOST

Relevant Words

Alfisols, Andisols, Aridisols, Compost, Entisols, Gelisols, Histosols, Hydroponics, Inceptisols, Leaching, Master horizons, Mollisols, Oxisols, Soil orders, Spodisols, Ultisols, Vertisols

Lab Objective

To research and identify the different types of soils sold in a local nursery, and compare them to find out the benefits for specific needs. To be able to make homemade compost by using daily waste.

Lab Assignment

- Visit a local nursery and identify the different types of soils sold.
- Compare them and describe pros and cons.
- Identify compost sold, and compare it with homemade version.
- Identify pH in soil and describe its importance for plant's growth.

Lecture Outlines

© Christos Georghiou/
Shutterstock.com

❖ Basic Soil Classifications by United States Department of Agriculture (USDA): Clay, Silt, Sand, and Gravel
❖ Soil Conservation
❖ Composting: *Nitrogen Rich Versus High Carbon Content*

SOIL AND COMPOST

Lecture Contents

© KittyVector/Shutterstock. com

Soil

Google an image of dirt. Google an image of soil. You'll find images of worms and organic matter among the images for soil. Soil is alive. A handful of healthy soil teems with billions of microorganisms. Each plays a critical role. Healthy plants require healthy soil. Of course, there are exceptions. Some plants are adaptive and hardy, and achieve health even in contaminated soils (as in mining and industrial reclamation sites). And some horticulturalists avoid soil all together (hydroponics).

Only 3% of the earths land surface is considered prime soil for cultivation. Another 8% of global land is considered adequate for cultivation, except with moderate to severe limitations as to which plants grow there. This means food for some seven billion people must come from 11% of our farmable global land (https://www.nrcs.usda.gov/wps/portal/nrcs/detail/soils/use/?cid=nrcs142p2_054028).

Yet soil degradation is happening at an alarming rate. One-third of the earth's soil has lost its fertility or is otherwise not cultivatable. All included, we have degraded global soils equivalent to the land of United States and Canada combined. Precious soil is blown in the wind, and lost in rains and floods. It is polluted, compacted, covered, and removed for development. Salts build up due to irrigation practices. Farmable land is lost to war and land mines. Fertility is lost by poor practices and extensive monocultures.

According to the UN Convention to Combat Desertification (UNCCD) about 12 million hectares of arable soil are lost on a global basis each year (https://knowledge.unccd.int/topics/land-degradation-neutrality). That means 33,000 hectares a day. That is 23 hectares per minute. A hectare to acre conversion brings us to 57 acres per minute. A football field is 1.3 acres. That's about 44 football fields of degraded soil per minute . . . a staggering thought. Worse, soil is not a renewable resource. Not in a human's lifetime at least. It takes about 100 years to form an inch of topsoil, and it varies depending on climate, vegetation, and other soil forming factors (https://www.nrcs.usda.gov/wps/portal/nrcs/detail/wa/soils/?cid=nrcs144p2_036333).

Soil has many important roles. To a plants person, the soil is something in which we grow. To an architect or engineer, it is something on which we build. To a soil scientist, ecologist, and naturalist, it is a living, functioning ecosystem. A handful of healthy soil has billions of microorganisms in it. Soil is a living ecosystem that is constantly interacting with climate, organisms, and time.

SOIL AND COMPOST

Lecture Contents (*continued*)

Soil (*continued*)

The USDA defines soil as "a natural body comprised of solids (minerals and organic matter), liquid, and gases that occurs on the land surface, occupies space, and is characterized by one or both of the following: horizons, or layers, that are distinguishable from the initial material as a result of additions, losses, transfers, and transformations of energy and matter or the ability to support rooted plants in a natural environment." For purposes of classification, the lower boundary of soil is arbitrarily set at 200 cm (https:// www.nrcs.usda.gov/wps/portal/nrcs/detail/soils/edu/?cid=nrcs142p2_054280).

Soil is formed by a combination of processes over time. As defined earlier, those processes include *additions*, *deletions*, *transfers*, and *transformations*.

Additions occur when things fall, drift, flood, or slide onto the land surface. Leaves fall. Manures are dropped. Animals fall (upon death). Trees fall and decompose. Sediment is left when flood waters recede. Topsoil is deposited from dust storms far away. These elements are mixed into the living soil with the aid of macro (large) and microorganisms.

Deletions occur with the erosive forces of wind and water. Deletions occur in land and mud slides. Deletions of organic matter and topsoil occur in widespread tilling practices. Plants take up (and thus delete) nutrients and when harvested and shipped off, there is no soil nutrient recycled back in.

Transfers are the downward movement of soluble materials (leaching). Nutrients are moved vertically through soil layers. This occurs more pronounced in areas of high rainfall and flooding.

Transformations include chemical weathering of sand, and formation of clay minerals, transformation of coarse organic material into humus. Sedimentary rock is turned to metamorphic rock. Rock is broken down into soil particles. Volcanic ash weathers into clay particles.

Soil is made up of six distinct horizontal layers. The layers near the surface have been altered by the interactions of climate and living organisms. The deepest layers are devoid of animals, roots, or other biological activity. The presence or absence of a layer helps soil scientists to classify and name different soil types.

We then can study a soil profile and make educated land use decisions. These layers are called Master Horizons. They include an O, A, E, B, C, and R.

SOIL AND COMPOST

Lecture Contents (*continued*)

Soil (*continued*)

The O layer is the organic layer. The A layer is the mineral layer. The O and A comprise the layer of topsoil we are familiar with. The O layer can be thick and rich in humus, as in our nation's midsection. Or, as in a desert soil, the layer is almost totally absent.

The E is the eluvial layer where soluble materials leach away from. The B layer is the alluvial layer where leached materials are deposited to or accumulate in. The E and B layers comprise the subsoil.

The underlying rocky layers consist of a C layer (the zone of minimal formation) and the R layer (parent material and/or bedrock). The absence or presence of these layers and the thickness of each allows for naming and classifying different soils. Soil scientists have grouped the possible combination of layers to 12 distinctive groups called orders. These are the 12 soil orders, presented from least developed soils (recently formed) to oldest and most weathered, as follows:

Entisols are newly developed soils where there are lots of new materials, such as on a flood plain or bottom of steep slope. They are also found where the rate of erosion and deletion is greater than additions, as in a sand dune. They are recent, hence their name. They have a very thin A layer over a C layer (the B layer is absent). Entisols make up about 16% of the worlds ice-free land area.

Inceptisols are very similar to entisols, except they have a weakly developed B layer. Often found in semiarid to humid mountain areas, covering approximately 17% of the global ice-free lands.

Andisols are the only soil order that are defined by the parent material. These are soils formed in volcanic ash. They are found only around volcanic activity, and have a very unique high glass content (aluminum, iron, and silicate). They are very light soils and have a high plant-available water. They tend to erode easily, as other fine textured soils do. They are highly fertile soils (including where coffee is grown). Andisols cover approximately 1% of the earth's ice-free land space.

Gelisols soils are of permafrost regions. They support the tundra/lichen environment, and support important wildlife ecosystems. They have very poor structural support. The permafrost needs to remain frozen. Buildings are built on stilts, and pipelines are built above ground. Gelisols cover approximately 9% of the world's ice-free land area.

SOIL AND COMPOST

Lecture Contents (*continued*)

Soil (*continued*)

Histosols are found in wet swampy environments. Covering about 1% of the earth's ice-free land area, they are extremely important wildlife habitat. They are commonly called bogs, moors, peats, or mucks. They are often mined for the peat material. If they dry, they cause problems as they can shrink by 85%.

Aridisols are soils that are defined by dry climate, hence the name arid. The lack of moisture limits weathering and leaching that happens in other soils. You must have irrigation to grow plants on an aridisol. Irrigation can leave harmful salts behind as the water evaporates. Salt affects a plant's ability to uptake water. Salts lead to desertification. Aridisols occupy the deserts of the world and cover approximately 12% of the earth's ice-free land space.

Vertisols are clayey soils with high shrink/swell capacity. They can be productive for agriculture (they support grasslands) but are problematic for engineering. They cause more monetary damage annually than earthquake, flood, and tornadoes combined. They are very common in regions with pronounced wet and dry cycles. Vertisols cover approximately 2% of the earth's ice-free land surface.

Mollisols are the most extensive soils in the United States and also the most productive. Formerly native grasslands, they now support "America's bread basket." They show a deep, fertile A horizon, high in calcium, magnesium, and potassium. They make up approximately 7% of the earth's ice-free land surface.

Alfisols are similar to mollisols but do not have as thick of an A layer. They are generally forested, with mixed vegetation. High in fertility, low in engineering problems, and is a good all-around soil. Alfisols cover approximately 10% of the earth's ice-free land area.

Ultisols are similar but more weathered and acidic. More often of conifer forests, they are not well suited for agriculture. They make up 8% of the earth's ice-free land surface.

Spodisols are generally found in conifer forested lands with more moisture. The acids help to mobilize elements, which are thus leached out readily, leaving the spodisol with low fertility. Spodisols are the most photogenic with an assortment of rusts and colors. They are found on approximately 4% of the earth's ice-free land surface.

Lecture Contents (*continued*)

Soil (*continued*)

And finally, we have ***oxisols***. They are representative of soils of hot, humid environments with intense biochemical weathering. They are the oldest soils and are most highly weathered. Many minerals are gone. They are very red in color and are sometimes referred as "a pile of rust." Oxisols (heavily oxidized) cover approximately 8% of the earth's ice-free land surface.

The ideal soil is a mix of sand, silt, and clay. We classify such natural blend as a loam. An advantage of a sandy soil is that there is excellent drainage and resistance to compaction. But sandy soils are not high in fertility. Clay soils have higher fertility, but poor drainage. A loam has the advantages of each; both good drainage and fertility.

Clay soils have a high cation exchange capacity. A cation is a molecule with a positive charge. Clay particles have a negative charge. Cations like the plant nutrients calcium, magnesium, and potassium are thus held tightly to clay soils, giving them their increased fertility. Clay particles (only visible via an electron microscope) are small but numerous. They present an increased surface area for water molecules to adhere to. Clay soils therefore do not drain well. Clay soils have high plasticity. Unfortunately, however, the clay is thus easily compacted. Plant roots grow through the spaces in soil. Thus, a compacted soil will slow plant growth.

SOIL AND COMPOST

Lecture Contents (*continued*)

Soil (*continued*)

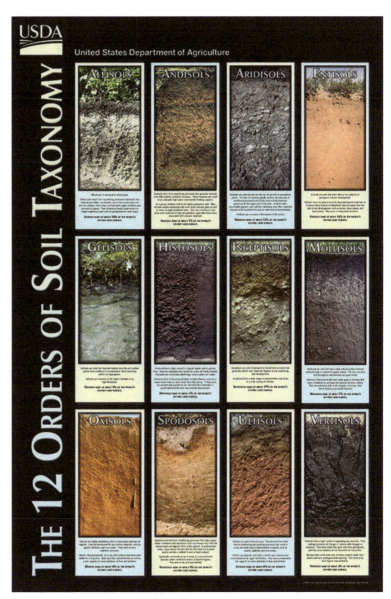

Source: USDA, https://www.nrcs.usda.gov/wps/portal/nrcs/detail/soils/survey/class/
data/?cid=nrcs142p2_053588.

SOIL AND COMPOST

Lecture Contents (*continued*)

Soil (*continued*)

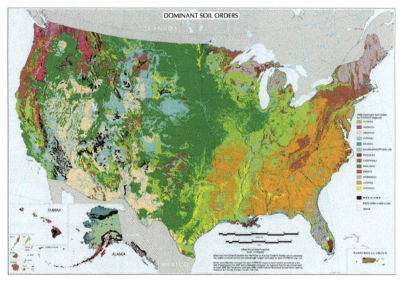

Source: USDA, https://www.nrcs.usda.gov/Internet/FSE_MEDIA/stelprdb1237749.pdf.

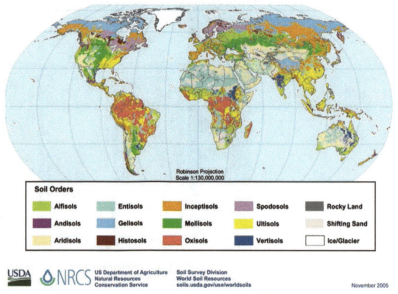

Source: USDA, https://www.nrcs.usda.gov/Internet/FSE_MEDIA/nrcs142p2_050722.jpg.

SOIL AND COMPOST

Lecture Contents (*continued*)

Soil (*continued*)

Soil

- Dynamic mixture of minerals, organic matter, microorganism, water, and air
- Basic soil types by USDA:
  - Clay
  - Silt
  - Sand
  - Gravel

- Mineral soil—Classified primarily by the size and quantity of mineral particles
- Organic soil—Predominately decaying organic matter

Horizons (Layers)

- A horizon—Topsoil (high level of organic matter)
- B and C horizons—Subsoil (low in organic matter and infertile)
- Hardpan—Layer of compacted soil (occasional presence)

Soil Components

- Physical
- Biological
- Chemical

Five Functions of Soil

- Organism habitat
- Water supply and purification
- Structural foundation
- Recycling nutrients
- Plant growing

SOIL AND COMPOST

Lecture Contents (*continued*)

Soil (*continued*)

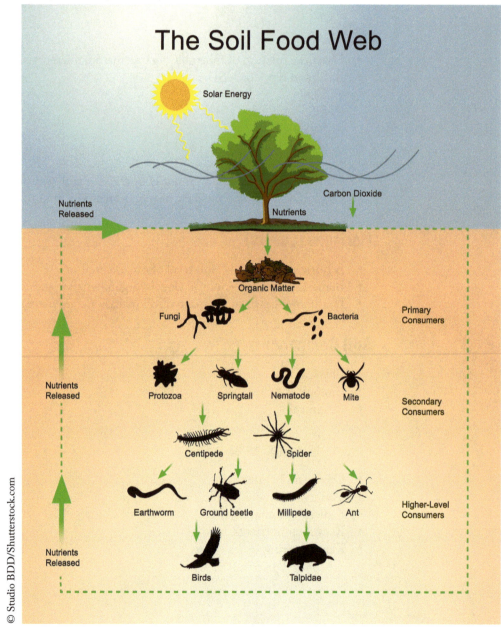

SOIL AND COMPOST

Lecture Contents (*continued*)

Soil (*continued*)

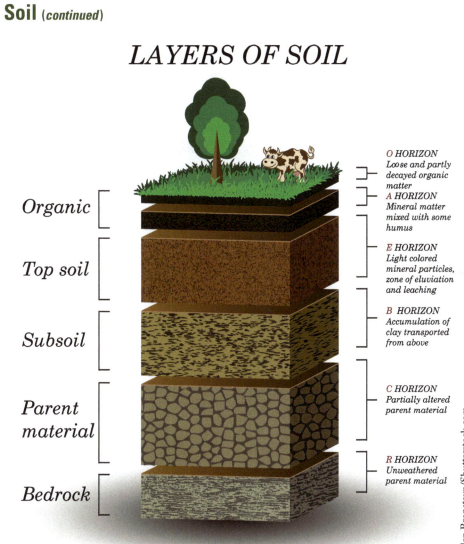

LAYERS OF SOIL

Organic

Top soil

Subsoil

Parent material

Bedrock

O HORIZON
Loose and partly decayed organic matter

A HORIZON
Mineral matter mixed with some humus

E HORIZON
Light colored mineral particles, zone of eluviation and leaching

B HORIZON
Accumulation of clay transported from above

C HORIZON
Partially altered parent material

R HORIZON
Unweathered parent material

© Ellen Bronstayn/Shutterstock.com

Lecture Contents (*continued*)

Soil (*continued*)

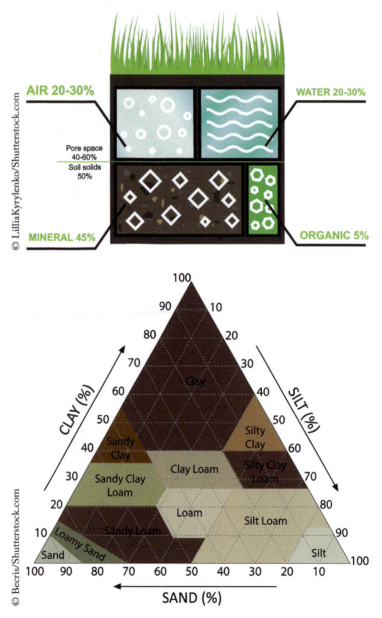

SOIL AND COMPOST

Lecture Contents (*continued*)

Soil (*continued*)

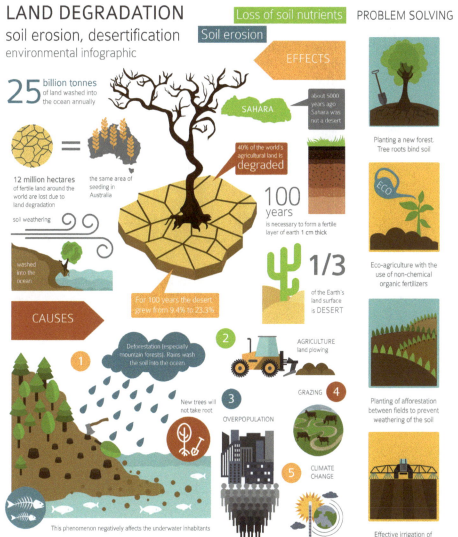

LAND DEGRADATION
soil erosion, desertification
environmental infographic

Loss of soil nutrients

Soil erosion

PROBLEM SOLVING

EFFECTS

25 billion tonnes of land washed into the ocean annually

SAHARA

about 5000 years ago Sahara was not a desert

40% of the world's agricultural land is **degraded**

100 years
is necessary to form a fertile layer of earth 1 cm thick

12 million hectares of fertile land around the world are lost due to land degradation

the same area of seeding in Australia

soil weathering

washed into the ocean

1/3 of the Earth's land surface is DESERT

For 100 years the desert grew from 9.4% to 23.3%

CAUSES

Deforestation (especially mountain forests). Rains wash the soil into the ocean

New trees will not take root

1

2 AGRICULTURE land plowing

3 OVERPOPULATION

GRAZING **4**

5 CLIMATE CHANGE

This phenomenon negatively affects the underwater inhabitants

Planting a new forest. Tree roots bind soil

ECO

Eco-agriculture with the use of non-chemical organic fertilizers

Planting of afforestation between fields to prevent weathering of the soil

Effective irrigation of sown areas

© Olha1981/Shutterstock.com

SOIL AND COMPOST

Lecture Contents (*continued*)

© Andrei Verner/
Shutterstock.com

Composting

Composting is an activity that will benefit sand and clay soils both. Compost is the recycling of the remains of decomposed organic matter. Organic matter aids sandy soils with fertility and moisture retention. Organic matter improves drainage in a clay soil. Composting saves trips to the landfill, thus lowering our carbon footprint. Optimal conditions for this process of decomposition include ample oxygen, and a mix of nitrogen- and carbon-rich materials. These nitrogen- and carbon-rich materials are also known as wet and dry organic materials, and/or green and brown organic materials.

Green/wet/nitrogen-rich materials include kitchen scraps (fruits and vegetable scraps, egg shells, coffee grounds and filters, but not meats, cheeses, and grease). Nitrogen-rich materials also include fresh grass trimmings and green yard waste. Brown/dry/carbon-rich materials include dried leaves, straw, shredded office paper, cardboard, wood chips, and so on. These ingredients are mixed in a bin or barrel and allowed to decompose. This is nature's way of recycling.

SOIL AND COMPOST

Lecture Contents (*continued*)

Composting (*continued*)

SOIL AND COMPOST

Relevant Links

TEDTalk

How to Grow a Forest in Your Backyard	https://www.ted.com/talks/shubhendu_sharma_how_to_grow_a_forest_in_your_backyard?utm_campaign=tedspread&utm_medium=referral&utm_source=tedcomshare
6 Ways Mushrooms Can Save the World	https://www.ted.com/talks/paul_stamets_on_6_ways_mushrooms_can_save_the_world?utm_campaign=tedspread&utm_medium=referral&utm_source=tedcomshare
A Vision for Sustainable Restaurants	https://www.ted.com/talks/arthur_potts_dawson_a_vision_for_sustainable_restaurants?utm_campaign=tedspread&utm_medium=referral&utm_source=tedcomshare

Wiki (Reference purpose only)

Compost	https://en.wikipedia.org/wiki/Compost
Soil	https://en.wikipedia.org/wiki/Soil

Others

Cornell Waste Management Institute	http://cwmi.css.cornell.edu/composting.htm
U.S. Environmental Protection Agency	https://www.epa.gov/recycle/composting-home
U.S. Department of Agriculture	https://www.nrcs.usda.gov/wps/portal/nrcs/detail/national/newsroom/features/?&cid=nrcs143_023537
Composting	http://www.solanacenter.org/sites/default/files/CIY%20FINAL.pdf

SOIL AND COMPOST

Quizzes

© Davidovka/Shutterstock.
com

1. Soil is formed by a combination of processes over time. As defined above, those processes include _____, _____, _____, and _____.

2. Identify number of soil layers, and, describe them briefly.

3. Write three examples of each for "brown" and "green" materials that can be composted.

Relevant Words

Analysis, Embodied energy, Essential elements, Eutrophication, Macronutrients, Micronutrients, Organic fertilizer, pH, Synthetic fertilizer

Lab Objective

To research and identify the different types of fertilizers sold in a local nursery, and, compare them to find out the benefits of specific nutrients. To be able to describe the benefits of using organic fertilizers.

Lab Assignment

- Visit a local nursery and identify the different types of fertilizer sold.
- Compare them and describe pros and cons.
- Identify organic fertilizer and describe the difference from synthetic fertilizer.
- Describe symptoms of nutritional deficiencies to their causes.

Lecture Outlines

© LynxVector/Shutterstock. com

❖ Macronutrients Versus Micronutrients
❖ Organic Versus Synthetic
❖ Negative Impact From Synthetic Fertilizer and How to Mitigate

CHAPTER 9   FERTILIZER

Lecture Contents

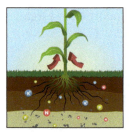

© Phuriwatt Seesuk/
Shutterstock.com

Fertilizer

Fertilizers are of immense importance to plant health. A complex system of plant functions relies on various key chemicals. These plant functions are called metabolism. Cell walls thicken. Leaves, roots, and stems are formed. Energy is produced. Flowers and scents are formed. Eggs, pollen, and seeds are formed. The list of various reactions going on is lengthy.

There are 118 elements on the Periodic Table. The table represents nature's ingredients list. Plants need 13 of the elements on the chart to thrive. The horticulturalist calls these elements the *13 essential elements.*

These elements are plant nutrients. For millions of years, these nutrients were plentiful and the earth was covered with healthy green plants. Today, we generally need to resupply these elements in fields and gardens that have lost their fertility. Plant nutrients are lost in the harvest process because the majority of plant parts for potential decomposition and recycling of nutrients is greatly disrupted.

We add these nutrients as amendments called fertilizers. Fertilizers that are from nature are called organic fertilizers. Fertilizers from factories are called synthetics. There is a vast difference in the embodied energy in each, and there is a dramatic difference each plays in soil ecosystem health. We compare and contrast these differences and discuss the advantages and disadvantages of each in this chapter, but let us first examine the role of each nutrient.

Of the 13 nutrients, six are classified as *macronutrients* (used in large quantity) and 7 are classified as *micronutrients* (used in small quantity). All are equally important, but used in vastly different quantities. A macronutrient can be supplied in 100 lb. quantities to an acre, for example, compared with an ounces-per-acre requirement of a micronutrient.

The macronutrients include *nitrogen (N), phosphorous (P), potassium (K), calcium (Ca), magnesium (Mg),* and *sulfur (S).* (Some texts treat calcium, magnesium, and sulfur as a separate category of "secondary nutrients"; this one does not.) The micronutrients include *iron (Fe), boron (B), chlorine (Cl), manganese (Mn), zinc (Zn), copper (Cu),* and *molybdenum (Mo).* The role of each nutrient is complex, and not yet fully understood. But each contributes to the vitality of a living plant, as discussed below.

Nitrogen is chiefly responsible for the production of chlorophyll, which is of vital importance in photosynthesis. As chlorophyll is a green pigment, nitrogen is said to induce

Lecture Contents (*continued*)

Fertilizer (*continued*)

lush green growth. If you want the golf course green, you apply a lot of nitrogen. But too much nitrogen and too much green growth come at the expense of flowering and fruiting. You might have the tallest, greenest tomato plant in the neighborhood, but with diminished fruit productivity. It is estimated that nitrogen is overused on a global basis by 25%. This leads to complex environmental problems. Synthetic nitrogen is fast and potent, but also fast to pollute. Nitrogen deficiencies appear as a yellowing of the lower (older) leaves and the plant can be spindly.

Phosphorus' chief contribution is flower and fruit set. Flower and fruit set means the flowers, and the resultant fruit do indeed stay on the stem until maturity. Some say phosphorous aids in seed production, which is essentially the same thing. You cannot have seed if the flower and/or fruit drops prematurely. In a phosphorous deficiency, leaf tips appear burnt. Older leaves turn a dark green or reddish purple.

Potassium plays a role in the movement of sugars, water, and nutrients, and general plant hardiness. It aids in the opening and closing of the stomata, which is critical for photosynthesis to function. It is soluble in water and can be easily leached, thus resulting in deficiencies. Older leaves may wilt and look scorched.

Calcium stimulates microbial activity and helps cell wall integrity. When deficient, new growth (at the top of the plant) is often distorted or irregularly shaped. Calcium deficiencies cause blossom end-rot.

Magnesium aids in the uptake of nitrogen, and as such aids photosynthesis.

Sulfur aids in the production of proteins. Proteins are involved in processes such as catalyzing chemical reactions. It gives onions and garlic their unique flavors. In a sulfur deficiency, newer leaves yellow first, sometimes followed by older leaves.

Iron plays a critical role in the synthesis of chlorophyll and is essential in the maintenance and functioning of the chloroplast. In an iron deficiency, yellowing occurs between the veins in the leaves. (The venation pattern stays green).

Boron helps keep the plant's cell walls strong and assists with cell division and hormone development. A deficiency in boron usually causes new growth to "abort", acting to "pinch" new growth and create tip dieback. Stems and petioles become brittle.

FERTILIZER

Lecture Contents (*continued*)

Fertilizer (*continued*)

Chlorine compliments and serves to balance the presence of potassium in its role of contributing to the opening and closing of the stomata. Chloride also aids in the water splitting phase of photosynthesis.

Manganese helps with the utilization of nitrogen in the plant and is thus noted as contributing to the process of photosynthesis. Deficiencies are easily confused with iron deficiencies, as the space between the leaf venation is yellowed. There will also be a reduction in the size of the plant's leaves, stems, and fruits.

Zinc aids in the absorption of water and nutrients from the soil; an obviously critical role. Zinc deficiencies are shown in stunted growth as a result. (smaller size of plants may occur as a result of reduced growth or inter-node elongation.)

Copper aids in the formation of lignin, which in addition to cellulose are the main constituents in wood. Lignin helps plants strengthen their stems and makes vegetables firm and crunchy. In a copper deficiency, leaves are dark green and the plant's growth is stunted.

Molybdenum is utilized in redox reactions. Redox reactions are chemical transformations involving reduction and oxidation. Breaking down sugar molecules into usable energy is a reduction process. Breaking down nitrogen into nitrates (the form plants utilize) is a redox reaction. Molybdenum also aides the process wherein nitrogen fixing plants can absorb atmospheric nitrogen into their roots (via a symbiotic relationship with fungi at root nodule). Molybdenum aids this process. Molybdenum deficiencies are similar to nitrogen deficiencies with a yellowing of the older leaves.

Information on deficiencies taken from *Guide to Symptoms of Plant Deficiencies*, University of Arizona, July 2018 (https://extension.arizona.edu/sites/extension.arizona.edu/files/pubs/az1106.pdf). Deficiencies, it should be noted, can occur even when nutrients are plentiful, if the soil chemistry is too acidic or too alkaline. A measure of the soils' acidity (on a scale of 0–14) is known as its pH; the lower numbers indicating acidity, and the higher indicating alkalinity. Plants are unable to take in nutrients if the pH is too high or low. Most plants thrive in a neutral pH at 7.

FERTILIZER

Lecture Contents (*continued*)

Fertilizer: Organic Versus Synthetic

Understanding that nutrients are crucial, it is important then, to determine their source. Should one choose organic or synthetic? We examine the advantages and disadvantages of each, in the following section.

First, it is important to recognize that plant nutrients from organic sources are not always initially present in a chemical form that the plant can utilize. Nitrogen, for example, is needed in large quantity. It is present in manure in a variety of forms, most of which gradually convert to plant-available ammonium and nitrate. Leaf litter contains nitrogen as well. But it isn't until the leaves are decomposed with the aid of worms and microorganisms that the nitrogen is made available to the plant. Worm castings (worm feces) are thus an excellent form of nutrient supply. Worms facilitate the needed chemical conversion. These are gradual conversions. Hence, organic sources are not "fast-acting".

Synthetic (factory made) forms of plant nutrients are already converted (in the factory) to a form readily available to plants. That is why synthetic fertilizers are indeed fast-acting. While some call fast-acting an advantage, some also point out synthetics are quick to pollute.

As stated earlier, macronutrients are needed in large quantity. By law, the amount of nitrogen, phosphorous, and potassium must be marked on the label of the fertilizer packaging. The percentages of N, P, and K must be clearly shown. This labeling is called the analysis. An advantage of synthetic fertilizers is that their analysis is higher (more potency) and the analysis can be customized. An analysis of a general purpose synthetic fertilizer is typically around 14–14–14 (compared with dry steer manure of 2–1.5–2.2). A general purpose synthetic lawn fertilizer analysis might read 20–0–8 (high in nitrogen for lush green growth, no need for fruit and flower set, yet contributes to disease resistance).

Embodied energy is known as the hidden cost of manufacturing. Hidden costs include the amount of resources used, the wastes generated, and the impact of a product on the environment. Synthetic fertilizers are disadvantaged because they have a high embodied energy. Nitrogen produced in a factory consumes a great deal of energy (one-fourth of our nation's supply of natural gas). Nitrogen factories are explosive and toxic.

Impact on soil resources is a major hidden cost of synthetics. As mentioned in Chapter 8, organic matter is healthy for soil and the microorganisms in it. Synthetics on the other hand are not beneficial to soil and its ecosystem. Synthetics degrade soil habitat.

FERTILIZER

Lecture Contents (*continued*)

Fertilizer: Organic Versus Synthetic (*continued*)

An abundance of fast-acting nitrogen initiates a breakdown of soil biodiversity. Nitrogen-fixing bacteria are diminished because they are not needed. Instead, activity of nitrogen-consuming organisms is increased. The nitrogen-consuming organisms speed the decomposition of soil-building organic matter and humus. As organic matter decreases, the physical structure of the soil and its water holding capacity are diminished. With less pore space and less of their sponge-like qualities, soils are less efficient at storing water and air. Thus, irrigation water is needed. Water leaches through and washes nutrients away that no longer have effective substrate on which to cling. With less available oxygen, the growth of soil microbiology slows, and the intricate ecosystem of biological exchanges breaks down. (https://grist.org/article/2010-02-23-new-research-synthetic-nitrogen-destroys-soil-carbon-undermines/).

Eutrophication is another hidden cost. It is characterized by an excess of nutrients in a waterway. Synthetic nitrogen is the leading culprit. Eutrophication leads to harmful algae bloom (HAB). HABs, when decomposing, rob nearby waters of oxygen, creating a dead-zone (an area of hypoxic water). The dead-zone in the Gulf of Mississippi is presently estimated at 7,000 to 8,000 square miles in size.

Phosphorous and potassium are mined before they are factory processed. Mining, and its disruptive forces on the landscape, is indeed an element of embodied energy, with respect to synthetics.

Organic sources of nitrogen, phosphorous, and potassium are not mined or manufactured. They are derived from natural sources including cow, sheep, rabbit, horse, and poultry manures; ancient deposits of bat and bird guanos; worm castings; bone; blood; and feather meal. There is no hidden cost to gather rabbit or poultry manure.

Organic nutrients are sometimes bulky (manures and compost) and smell bad (fish emulsion). Some might consider the slow-acting nature as a disadvantage, but others argue they are also thus slower to pollute. There is difference in cost as well. Synthetics are fast, cheap, and easy. Organics can be more expensive. Worm castings are $40 a bag. Fish emulsion is $40 a gallon. Some might get their horse manure for free from the local stable, for example, and make their own compost (Chapter 8).

FERTILIZER

Lecture Contents (*continued*)

Fertilizer: Application Techniques

Fertilizers can be incorporated into the garden or container potting mix prior to planting. This is referred to as preplanting incorporation. Top dressing is broadcasting a fertilizer over the top of existing plants (such as using a spreader to broadcast fertilizer pellets over turf). Side dressing is appropriate where edibles are used. A row of fertilizer is placed in a narrow strip adjacent to the planting. The drill hole method or needle feeding methods allow for fertilizers to be put at feeder root depth (about 18 in.).

Mineral Nutrients

Macronutrients: Nutrients used in large quantities

1. Nitrogen (N)–Primary fertilizer ingredient
2. Phosphorus (P)–Primary fertilizer ingredient
3. Potassium (K)–Primary fertilizer ingredient
4. Calcium (Ca)
5. Magnesium (Mg)
6. Sulfur (S)

Nitrogen (N)

- When lacking, slow growing and loss of deep green color
- Stimulates rapid vegetative growth
- High level of nitrogen
  - Great for the leaves, not for flowers and fruits
  - Ill-timed growth resulting in cold injury
  - Can cause root damage
- The form of nitrate to remain dissolved in the soil water—To leach from the soil with heavy rainfall
  - Sandy soil: Slow release or frequent small applications of quick release
  - Clay soil: Quick release

FERTILIZER

Lecture Contents (*continued*)

Fertilizer (*continued*)

Phosphorus (P)

- Important for flowering, fruiting, root development, disease resistance and maturation
- Insoluble in the soil water – reacting with aluminum, iron, calcium, and, forming various compounds unusable by plants
- To maintain enough in the soil water – pH 6-7, high organic matter
- To be applied in the root zone
- Used as transplant or starter fertilizer (low nitrogen and potassium, high phosphorus) as a liquid form

Potassium (K)

- Essential for starch formation, movement of sugar, formation of chlorophyll, flower and fruit coloring, opening & closing of leaf stoma
- Should be in usable form, due to leaching fast in heavy rainfall
- Overdose of potassium
    - Waste with no benefits in plant growth or appearance
    - Burn or injure plants by killing the root tips
- Frequent, small amount application

Micronutrients: Trace elements, important but used in small quantities

1. Iron (Fe)
2. Copper (Cu)
3. Zinc (Zn)
4. Boron (B)
5. Molybdenum (Mo)
6. Chlorine (Cl)
7. Cobalt (Co)

Lecture Contents *(continued)*

Fertilizer *(continued)*

FERTILIZER

Lecture Contents (*continued*)

Fertilizer (*continued*)

Nutrients in Organic Fertilizer

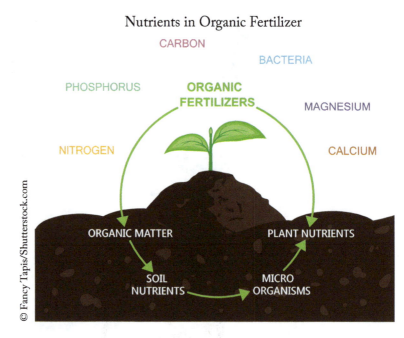

Understanding the Fertilizer Label

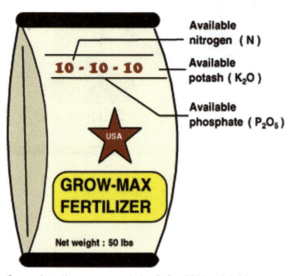

Source: http://www.ncagr.gov/cyber/kidswrld/plant/label.htm

All fertilizer labels have three bold numbers. The first number is the amount of nitrogen (N), the second number is the amount of phosphate (P_2O_5) and the third number is the amount of potash (K_2O). These three numbers represent the primary nutrients (nitrogen(N) - phosphorus(P) - potassium(K)).

This label, known as the fertilizer grade, is a national standard.

A bag of 10–10–10 fertilizer contains 10 percent nitrogen, 10 percent phosphate and 10 percent potash.

FERTILIZER

Lecture Contents (*continued*)

Fertilizer (*continued*)

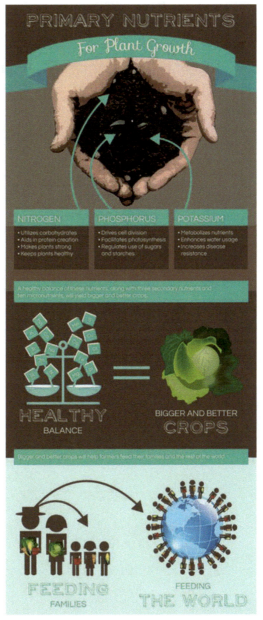

Source: From IFDC copyright © 2015. Used with permission.

FERTILIZER

Lecture Contents (*continued*)

Fertilizer (*continued*)

Nutrient Deficiency

- Majority of nutrients available between pH 6.5 and 7.0
- To correct micronutrient deficiencies, proper soil pH is essential.
- "Chelated" form of micronutrients—Most effective
- Optimum soil moisture and warm temperature to decrease micronutrient deficiency

Nutrient	Symptoms	Causes	Solutions
Boron	Distorted leaves	Soil pH <6.8 or >5.5; low organic matter	To add sulfur
Copper	Yellowish thin leaves	High pH	To add sulfur
Iron	Light green or yellow youngest leaves	High pH, low organic matter, excessive P	To add sulfur, compost
Manganese	Mottled yellowish young leaves	High pH	To add sulfur
Molybdenum	Distorted, curling leaves	Low pH	To add lime
Zinc	Yellow leaves, rust spots	High pH, wet soil, excessive P	To add sulfur

FERTILIZER

Lecture Contents (*continued*)

Fertilizer (*continued*)

NUTRIENT ELEMENT DEFICIENCY									
Symptom	**Deficient Element**								
	N	**P**	**K**	**Mg**	**Fe**	**Cu**	**Zn**	**B**	**Mo**
Curling-over leaves				×					
Curling-under leaves			×			×			
Wrinkling/Curling young leaves			×				×	×	×
Dropping of old leaves	×								
Dark green/purple leaves & stems		×							
Pale green leaves	×								×
Dead growing tips			×					×	
Soft stems	×		×						
Hard/brittle stems		×	×						
Stunted leave growth	×	×							
Stunted root growth		×							
Tip-burning old leaves	×						×		
Tip-burning young leaves								×	
Yellowing between veins				×					
Yellowing of middle leaves									×
Yellowing of old leaves	×		×	×			×		
Yellowing of young leaves					×				
Molting							×		
Necrosis			×	×	×		×		
Spindly	×								
Wilting						×			

FERTILIZER

Relevant Links

TEDTalk
Simple Solution to Phosphorus Crisis https://www.ted.com/talks/mohamed_hijri_a_simple_solution_to_the_coming_phosphorus_crisis?utm_campaign=tedspread&utm_medium=referral&utm_source=tedcomshare

Wiki (Reference purpose only)
Fertilizer https://en.wikipedia.org/wiki/Fertilizer

Others
California Fertilization Guidelines https://apps1.cdfa.ca.gov/FertilizerResearch/docs/Guidelines.html

Reading a Fertilizer Label http://www.forestry.alabama.gov/Publications/TREASURED_Forest_Magazine/2005-2006%20Fall-Winter/It's%20All%20in%20The%20Numbers%20Reading%20a%20Fertilizer%20Label.pdf

Environmental Protection Agency https://www.epa.gov/agriculture/agriculture-nutrient-management-and-fertilizer

International Fertilizer Development https://ifdc.org/our-work/
Center (IFDC)
One Straw Revolution http://www.onestrawrevolution.net/One_Straw_Revolution/One-Straw_Revolution.html

FERTILIZER

Quizzes

© Davidovka/Shutterstock.com

1. Plant nutrients are categorized as _____ and _____. Identify plant nutrient elements in each category.

2. Describe embodied energy, and, give an example of embodied energy in the production of synthetics.

3. What are three examples of organic fertilizer sources?

CHAPTER 10

PEST AND DISEASE

Relevant Words

Earth Day, Entomology, Environmental Protection Agency (EPA), Fungicide, Insecticide, Integrated Pest Management (IPM), Pathogen, *Rachel Carson (Silent Spring)*, Rodenticide

Lab Objective

To research and identify common pests and diseases that may affect a plant's health. To research and find sustainable solutions to common pests and diseases.

Lab Assignment

- Identify pest and/or disease that may have been affecting your plants.
- Research how to mitigate pest and disease identified.
- Research and identify the sustainable approach to mitigate pest and disease.
- Describe the phenomena of metamorphosis.

Lecture Outlines

❖ Integrated Pest Management (IPM)
❖ Organic Versus Synthetic Treatment for Disease
❖ Benefits From Sustainable Treatment Against Pest and Disease

© Andi Muhammad Hasbi
H/Shutterstock.com

PEST AND DISEASE

Lecture Contents

© Vidtorya170377/
Shutterstock.com

Pest

Pests create havoc in the garden. They dine, dig, devour, and deform. They tunnel, stunt, and steal. Invertebrates (insects, mites, or snails) and vertebrates (birds, rodents, or other mammals) are an absolute nuisance in the garden and urban farm. Pests are often controlled by toxic chemical, especially in years past. Insecticides and other poisons have proven quite effective, but with high impact on ecosystems worldwide.

There are some 900,000 species of insects, but only a small portion is considered pests. Pests are those that cause disease and economic harm. Pests are organisms that damage or interfere with desirable plants in our urban farms, gardens, orchards, and landscapes.

In a natural, fully functioning ecosystem, potential pests are generally kept under control by natural forces. A particular insect population might be kept under control by severe winter freeze. A natural wildfire could eradicate a troublesome pest. Predatory organisms could keep insect populations in balance. Plants native to a region can adapt over time to defend themselves from pests by producing toxins, armaments, pollination strategies, and such.

But when plant, insect, and/or soil are outside of their native habitat, the natural mechanism of pest control is usually lost as well. Take, for example, the plight of the American elm (*Ulmus americana*). A once grand monarch of the American forest and important shade tree in landscape and garden, it was all but wiped out on the North American continent in the 1930s because of a disease carried by a boring insect from overseas. There were no normal barriers to keep the borer in check in its new home on this continent. Imperial expansion, world travel, and trade have exacerbated the problem, as unwanted species have stowed onboard shipments and in luggage.

The management of pests is as old as agriculture. But with the industrialization and mechanization of farming in the 18th and 19th centuries, pest management reached new heights. Botanically derived insecticides like pyrethrum and derris were widely used. Synthetic insecticides were introduced in the 20th century.

A Swiss chemist discovered dichlorodiphenyltrichloroethane (DDT) in 1939. The U.S. government instructed its troops to sprinkle the cheap, easy DDT powder in their sleeping bags to prevent disease carried by insects. American agriculture soon followed suit with widespread use of this "miraculous" insecticide.

PEST AND DISEASE

Lecture Contents (*continued*)

Pest (*continued*)

But in 1944, researchers at the U.S. Public Health Service warned, "The toxicity of DDT combined with its cumulative actions and absorbability through the skin places a definite health hazard in its use." It was also reported, but not widely known, that DDT was killing beneficial insects and wildlife as well.

By this time, there were thousands of insecticide products on the market. In 1947, federal legislation was devised, not to protect the environment (and humans) from poisons, but to protect the public from fraudulent claims. The Federal Insecticide, Fungicide and Rodenticide Act (FIFRA) was passed. The law, while not addressing bioaccumulative environmental dangers, at least brought the government into the business of regulating new and dangerous chemicals. In the first 5 years of FIFRA's existence, companies registered almost 10,000 new pesticides (https://livinghistoryfarm.org/farminginthe40s/pests_07.html).

The ecology movement arrived in the 1960s in the footsteps of massive antiwar protests. Rachel Carson's book entitled *The Silent Spring* (published in 1962) gained congress and others' attention. It gave accounts of songbirds falling out of the air dead after consuming worms that had eaten DDT-contaminated leaves.

The first Earth Day was celebrated on April 22, 1970. The Environmental Protection Agency (EPA) was established in December of that same year. A significant revision was made to FIFRA in 1972 by passage of the Federal Environmental Pesticide Control Act (FEPCA). It expanded the authority of the EPA to oversee the use of pesticides with emphasis on protecting the health of humans and the environment.

President Richard M. Nixon directed federal agencies to advance the concept and application of **Integrated Pest Management (IPM)** strategies in 1972 as well. IPM strategies are those strategies with an emphasis on less toxic methods. President Bill Clinton reemphasized a commitment to less toxic methods with the launching of the Clinton Initiative in 1993. He launched a goal that 75% of U.S. farmland would be managed under the principles of IPM by the year 2000.

In 2002, the U.S. Department of Agriculture (USDA) launched the National Road Map for IPM. It was updated in 2004, and again in October 2013, with a call for increased communication among IPM practitioners nationwide. The document defines IPM as follows:

PEST AND DISEASE

Lecture Contents (continued)

Pest (continued)

"Integrated Pest Management (IPM) is a science based, decision making process that identifies and reduces risks from pests and pest management related strategies. IPM coordinates the use of pest biology, environmental information, and available technology to prevent unacceptable levels of pest damage by the most economical means, while minimizing risk to people, property, resources, and the environment. IPM provides an effective strategy for managing pests in all arenas from developed agricultural, residential, and public lands to natural and wilderness areas. IPM provides an effective, all encompassing, low-risk approach to protect resources and people from pests" (http://www.ipmcenters.org/IPMRoadMap.pdf).

Recommended strategies of IPM are discussed later. There is, however, a critical step before implementing any pest management strategy. First, one must know the plant, and one must know the pest. Gone are the days when broad-spectrum insecticides were used to "kill anything that moves." We must be prudent, and narrow the target as appropriate. Identifying the pest can be difficult, but it is fairly easy to at least identify whether it is a chewer or a sucking pest by the damage done.

Chewing pests tear holes obviously. An experienced entomologist (a scientist who studies insects) can identify a pest by the pattern of tearing. Some insects produce an irregular tear. Some produce a perfect sphere. Some chew on the margin of the leaf. Some chew on the midrib. Some chew a tunnel through the mesophyll. Look for the pest. If it's not evident, check at night. It might be nocturnal (occurring at night).

Sucking pests leave marks called "puckering." Puckering is a deformation caused when sugars are sucked out of the phloem. Sucking pests leave not tears, but a pattern of sunken blemishes.

Examples of chewing pests follow:

Grasshoppers (*Schistocerca americana*) are likely the oldest living group of chewing herbivorous insects, dating back to around 250 million years ago. Grasshoppers eat large quantities of foliage both as adults and during their development, and can be serious pests of arid land and prairies. Pasture, grain, forage, vegetable, and other crops can be affected. Grasshoppers often bask in the sun, and thrive in warm sunny conditions, so drought stimulates an increase in grasshopper populations (http://ipm.ucanr.edu/PMG/PESTNOTES/pn74103.html).

PEST AND DISEASE

Lecture Contents (*continued*)

Pest (*continued*)

Leaf miners are the larval (maggot) stage of an insect family that feeds between the upper and the lower surfaces of leaves. On heavily infested plants, it is not uncommon to find six or more maggots per leaf. Although damage can restrict plant growth, resulting in reduced yields and loss of vigor, healthy plants can tolerate considerable injury. Host plants include beans, blackberries, cabbage, lettuce, peppers, and a variety of ornamental flowers, citrus trees, and shrubs (https://www.planetnatural.com/pest-problem-solver/houseplant-pests/leafminer-control/).

Snails and *slugs* are among the most destructive pests found in gardens and landscapes. The brown garden snail (*Cornu aspersum*) is the most common snail causing problems in California gardens. It was introduced from France during the 1850s for use as food. Both snails and slugs are members of the mollusk phylum and are similar in structure and biology, except that slugs lack the snail's external spiral shell. These mollusks move by gliding along on a muscular "foot." This muscle constantly secretes mucus, which facilitates their movement and later dries to form the silvery slime trail that signals the recent presence of either pest (http://ipm.ucanr.edu/PMG/PESTNOTES/pn7427.html).

Earwigs. The introduced European earwig is the most common of several earwig species that can occur in citrus. Adults are about 0.75 in. long, reddish brown, and have a pair of prominent tail appendages (cerci) that resemble forceps. Most species have wings under short, hard wing covers, but earwigs seldom fly. Males have stout, strongly curved cerci that are widely separated at the base while females possess slender, straight pinchers that are close together. Earwigs use these cerci to protect themselves and to grab and hold prey. Immature earwigs resemble small, wingless adults.

Earwigs feed mostly at night and hide during the day. Common hiding places include bark crevices, mulch, topsoil, protected (touching) plant parts, and under trunk wraps. Females lay masses of 30 or more eggs in soil. Nymphs are whitish and remain in soil until their first molt, after which they darken and begin emerging from the soil in search of food. Earwigs generally have one or two generations a year. They can be active year-round (http://ipm.ucanr.edu/PMG/r107304211.html).

Caterpillars are the larval stage of members of the butterflies and moths' families, and as a rule are voracious feeders. Many of them are among the most serious of horticultural pests. They outgrow their skin and shed it several times. After the last shedding, the caterpillar fastens to a branch and enters the pupa or chrysalis stage; moth caterpillars

PEST AND DISEASE

Lecture Contents (*continued*)

Pest (*continued*)

use a silk thread from their silk glands to spin a protective cocoon. Inside the cocoon, the pupa goes through a process called metamorphosis. The caterpillar's six front legs transform into the adult insect's legs, the other "prolegs" disappear, wings grow, and the insect emerges as a beautiful moth or butterfly (https://switchzoo.com/profiles/caterpillar.htm).

Bark beetle adults are small, cylindrical, hard-bodied insects about the size of a grain of rice. Most species are dark red, brown, or black. Their larvae are known as borers. They are common pests of conifers (such as pines) and some attack broadleaf trees. Over 600 species occur in the United States and Canada with approximately 200 in California alone. The most common species infesting pines in urban landscapes and at the wildland–urban interface in California are the engraver beetles, the red turpentine beetle, and the western pine beetle (http://ipm.ucanr.edu/PMG/PESTNOTES/pn7421.html). Generally, climate change is likely to mean that many wood-boring pests of cold northern zones will become more destructive, since higher temperatures will increase winter survival.

Grubs are large C-shaped beetle larvae that feed on roots of turf grass plants. These grubs are white, up to 1 in (2.5 cm) in length, with dark translucent dorsal stripes, brown head capsules and legs, and a characteristic pattern of bristles on the underside of the posterior end of the abdomen (http://ipm.ucanr.edu/PMG/r785301311.html).

Common sucking pests are discussed in the following paragraphs:

Aphids are small, soft-bodied insects with long slender mouthparts that they use to pierce stems, leaves, and other tender plant parts and suck out fluids. Almost every plant has one or more aphid species that occasionally feed on it. Many aphid species are difficult to distinguish from one another; however, management of most aphid species is similar (http://ipm.ucanr.edu/PMG/PESTNOTES/pn7404.html).

Whiteflies are tiny, sap-sucking insects that may become abundant in vegetable and ornamental plantings, especially during warm weather. They excrete sticky honeydew and cause yellowing or death of leaves. Outbreaks often occur when the natural biological control is disrupted. Management is difficult once populations are high (http://ipm.ucanr.edu/PMG/PESTNOTES/pn7401.html).

PEST AND DISEASE

Lecture Contents (*continued*)

Pest (*continued*)

Mealybugs are soft, oval, wax-covered insects that feed on many plants in garden, landscape, and indoor settings. Usually found in colonies, they are piercing–sucking insects, closely related to soft scales but lack the scale covers. Like soft scales, they can produce abundant honeydew and are often associated with black sooty mold. Mealybugs are favored by warm weather and thrive in areas without cold winters or on indoor plants (http://ipm.ucanr.edu/PMG/PESTNOTES/pn74174.html).

Scales are sucking insects that insert their tiny, straw-like mouthparts into bark, fruit, or leaves, mostly on trees and shrubs and other perennial plants. Some scales can seriously damage their host, while other species do no apparent damage to plants even when scales are very abundant. The presence of scales can be easily overlooked, in part because they do not resemble most other insects (http://ipm.ucanr.edu/PMG/PESTNOTES/pn7408.html).

Mites are common pests in landscapes and gardens that feed on many fruit trees, vines, berries, vegetables, and ornamental plants. Although related to insects, mites aren't insects but members of the arachnid class along with spiders and ticks. Spider mites, also called web-spinning mites, are the most common mite pests and among the most ubiquitous of all pests in the garden and on the farm (http://ipm.ucanr.edu/PMG/PESTNOTES/pn7405.html).

Thrips are tiny, slender insects with fringed wings. They feed by puncturing the epidermal (outer) layer of host tissue and sucking out the cell contents, which results in stippling, discolored flecking, or silvering of the leaf surface. Thrips feeding is usually accompanied by black varnish-like flecks of frass (excrement). Pest species are plant feeders that discolor and scar leaf, flower, and fruit surfaces, and distort plant parts or vector plant pathogens. Many species of thrips feed on fungal spores and pollen and are often innocuous. However, pollen feeding on plants such as orchids and African violets can leave unsightly pollen deposits and may reduce flower longevity (http://ipm.ucanr.edu/PMG/PESTNOTES/pn7429.html).

It may be difficult to identify all the diverse plants in your region. Many even are native to faraway lands. It is recommended, however, that you at least know the plants in your garden or local community. It helps you connect with nature, which benefits your well-being. It also helps you select an appropriate pest management strategy. Inquire with the local Master Gardeners office. An extension of each state's university system, their

PEST AND DISEASE

Lecture Contents (*continued*)

Pest (*continued*)

offices offer a wealth of information on local plant health and pest control. Numerous apps are now available that help identify a plant with a simple photo. Or take a piece of stem with leaves and/or flower to your local nursery and ask for help. Find out about the plants among you; respect where you dwell.

The use of well-adapted plants is the first strategy of IPM. Plants adapt to their environment over time. They adapt to nutrient-rich soils in locations where soils are nutrient rich. Other plants adapt to bland soils. Plants in arid climates and higher altitudes have adapted to having smaller leaves (so that they lose less water).

Plants also adapt to region's pests at hand. The desert tobacco plant (*Nicotiana attenuata*) is normally pollinated by the nocturnal hawkmoth *Manduca sextah*. Thus, it usually opens it flowers at night. But there is a problem with being pollinated by the hawkmoth. It lays eggs that hatch into caterpillars. The caterpillars dine heavily on the plant. In its own dramatic defense, the desert tobacco plant changes the shape and scent of its flowers, and to a daytime schedule for its flowers to open. This attracts pollination by hummingbird instead. These changes were observed in a 2-week period; a very quick adaptation. Plants that are native to a particular region have adapted over a long period of time and are generally far less appealing to pests.

A garden with well-adapted plants includes a garden with plants that are planted in the correct exposure, at the right time of year, as well. If you plant a tomato in shade, for example, the plant will be stressed, and pests will attack. Corn planted in the cool season when daylight hours are short will exhibit stress and will be loaded with pests. Choose your plants wisely. Plant them at the right time, and, in the right place with care.

A second IPM strategy involves the use of mechanical controls. The use of a barrier is one such example; a fence of chicken wire around a plant or garden will keep rabbits away. Deer netting or bird netting can be used quite easily. The latter two are not recommended if you have lizards in your garden. They often get tangled in the net and succumb.

Removal by hand is another example of the mechanical control strategy. Pay neighborhood youth 50 cents for each tomato hornworm they remove. Eliminate pests with a forceful spray of water from the garden hose. Use a trap instead of toxins. These are additional examples of the mechanical control strategy.

Lecture Contents (*continued*)

Pest (*continued*)

If beetles are particularly troublesome in late June, try planting earlier. Adjusting the planting and harvesting time is an ancient strategy. Fortunately, the tactic has been adopted by practitioners of IPM today.

The use of less toxic methods is also a critical component of an IPM approach. The use of soap as an insecticide or botanically derived insecticides like chrysanthemum oil and neem oil aids in pest control without threatening ground water supply with toxins. Biological controls such as the use of beneficial insects also fall under this category. Ladybug beetles (*Coccinella septempunctata*) devour aphids. The praying mantis (*Mantis religiosa*) will eat grasshoppers and many other harmful insects. Dried pellets of fox urine keep rabbits and squirrels away.

The acceptance of minor damage is another important strategy. A pest-free garden is not possible, nor is one desired. Insectivorous songbirds and beneficial insects need food too. A couple holes in your lettuce do not warrant an all-out chemical assault.

And finally, we include the use of chemicals as a last resort IPM option, but it must be emphasized that best practices call for a *prudent* use of chemicals. Chemicals, if used, must only be used according to the manufacturer's instructions. Any relevant codes of good practice should be observed and adhered to. Storage and/or disposal must be properly conceived. Broad-spectrum insecticides are exponentially more toxic. A narrow target or spectrum is therefore most desired.

Pests and diseases have been a nuisance to farmers since biblical times. And there are far many more pests than have been described herein. It is important to keep a keen eye on a garden or plant production scheme. Take actions to keep pathogens from becoming a problem, such as by using disease-resistant plants. Monitor gardens closely to ensure timely application of less toxic alternatives. IPM strategies work in the long term if we maintain diverse and healthy ecosystems.

Rather than simply eliminating any pests at hand, using IPM means you'll look at environmental factors that affect the pest and its ability to thrive. Armed with this information, one can create conditions that are unfavorable for the pest and do less harm to the garden ecosystem.

(*continued*)

PEST AND DISEASE

Lecture Contents (*continued*)

Pest (*continued*)

Source: Los Angeles County, Department of Agricultural Commissioner, https://acwm.lacounty.gov/wp-content/uploads/2018/05/FinalWANTEDno-website.pdf.

Lecture Contents (*continued*)

Pest (*continued*)

Pesticide in Groundwater

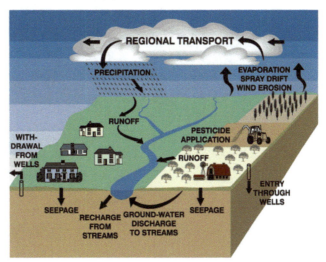

Source: USGS, https://pubs.usgs.gov/fs/2005/3087/.

Integrated Pest Management (IPM)

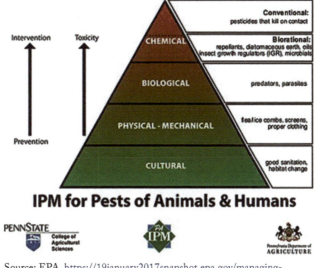

Source: EPA, https://19january2017snapshot.epa.gov/managing-pests-schools/definition-verifiable-school-ipm_.html.

Lecture Contents (*continued*)

Pest (*continued*)

What Is IPM?

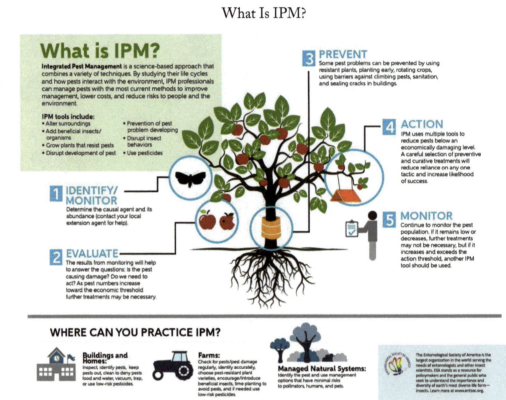

Source: https://www.maine.gov/dacf/php/integrated_pest_management/documents/IPMversusOPM document.pdf.

Lecture Contents (*continued*)

Pest (*continued*)

Plants Attracting Beneficial Insects

Plants that Attract Beneficial Insects		
Beneficial	**Pests**	**Plants/Habitat**
Assassin bug (Reduviidae family)	Many insects including flies and large caterpillars	Permanent plantings for shelter (e.g., windbreaks)
Bees-Butterflies (Many families)	None but important for pollination	Pea, borage, and aster families, milkweeds, butterfly bush, others
Braconid wasp (Braconidae family)	Armyworm, cabbageworm, codling moth, gypsy moth, European corn borer, aphid, caterpillars, and other insects	Nectar plants with small flowers, yarrow, sunflower, cowparsnip
Damsel bug (Nabidae family)	Aphid, thrips, leafhopper, treehopper, caterpillars	Aster family, yarrow, common boneset
Ground beetle (Carabidae family)	Slug, snail, cutworm, Colorado potato beetle, gypsy moth, caterpillars, weed seeds	Amaranth, bunch grasses, permanent plantings for shelter
Lacewing (Chrysopidae family)	Soft bodied insects including aphid, thrips, European corn borer, mealybug, scale, mite	Carrot and aster family (coreopsis, sunflowers, goldenrod)
Ladybug beetle (Coccinellidae family)	Aphid, spider mite, European corn borer, mealybug	Aster family, butterfly weed, native grasses, giant hyssop, cowparsnip, yarrow, black locust
Minute Pirate Bug (Anthocorid family)	Thrips, spider mite, leafhopper, corn earworm, small caterpillars, and other insects	Carrot and aster family (daisies, sunflowers, yarrow, goldenrod), blue elderberry, potentilla, giant hyssop, common boneset, and willows

(*continued*)

PEST AND DISEASE

Lecture Contents (*continued*)

Pest (*continued*)

Plants that Attract Beneficial Insects		
Beneficial	**Pests**	**Plants/Habitat**
Rove beetle (Staphylinidae family)	Aphid, nematode, flies	Native grasses, permanent plantings for shelter
Spider (Salticidae, Thomisidae, and other families)	Many insects	Carrot and aster family, giant hyssop
Spined soldier bug (*Podisus maculiventris*)	Armyworm, sawfly, Colorado potato beetle, Mexican bean beetle	Aster family (sunflowers, yarrow)
Tachinid fly (Tachinidae family)	Cutworm, armyworm, May beetle, gypsy moth, squash bug	Carrot and aster family, amaranth
Tiger beetle (Cicindelidae family)	Many insects	Amaranth, bunch grasses, permanent plantings for shelter
Chalcid wasps (many families including Trichogrammatidae)	Spruce budworm, cotton bollworm, tomato hornworm, corn earworm, corn borer, codling moth	Carrot and aster family (daisies, sunflowers, yarrow, goldenrod), potentilla, giant hyssop, cowparsnip, common boneset
Hover fly (Syrphidae family)	Aphid	Carrot and aster family (coreopsis, sunflowers, goldenrod), cowparsnip, common boneset

Source: https://www.fs.usda.gov/nac/buffers/docs/5/5.2ref.pdf.

Lecture Contents (*continued*)

Pest (*continued*)

Interplant to Attract Beneficial Insects

Source: https://www.usbg.gov/interplanting-pest-control.

PEST AND DISEASE

CHAPTER 10

Lecture Contents (*continued*)

© stockshoppe/
Shutterstock.com

Disease

Chewing and sucking pests can decimate a garden quickly and so too can plant disease. The study of plant disease is called plant pathology. The science includes disease identification, examination of the causes of disease, analysis of environmental conditions favoring disease, and disease prevention.

Disease is malfunctioning of a plant's physiological processes that results from an interference by pathogenic bacteria, virus, and/or fungi. These organisms cause plant diseases that reduce our ability to grow food, produce fiber and biofuels, and harm the economy. All plants, from citrus and grains to ornamental shrubs and forest trees, are susceptible to plant diseases.

Historically, consider *Phytophthora infestans*, a water mold that destroys the leaves and tubers of the potato plant (*Solanum tuberosum*). *Phytophthora infestans* was responsible for the Great Famine in Ireland in 1845 to 1859. One million people died of starvation because the potato crop was thoroughly destroyed in successive years.

Consider the killer fungus that has destroyed tens of thousands of trees along the banks of the *Canal du Midi* in France. Construction of this historic waterway started in 1667. It runs 155 miles (250 km) from the Atlantic to the Mediterranean. About 42,000 shade trees were planted along its banks in the 1830s to prevent erosion and evaporation. It has been designated as a UNESCO World Heritage site as a remarkable feat of engineering and living work of art.

In 2006, the trees began to succumb to a disease caused by a fungus. The fungus originated in the wood of a WWII ammunitions box. Of those trees, 15,000 have already been cut down; the remaining are in jeopardy. The wood must be burned in place (https://www.theguardian.com/world/2015/aug/17/more-plane-trees-felled-along-canal-du-midi-in-fight-against-killer-fungus).

Consider the 30 different species of tree that are in peril from the polyphagous shot hole borer currently in Southern California. As small as a sesame seed, the insect bores into the bark of Western sycamore (*Platanus racemosa*) and other prized local species. The larvae of the borer eat a fungus. The borer (parent) brings the fungus with them to the tree. The fungus kills the tree. At this writing, there is no remedy (no poison strong enough). The trees must be removed, and the wood must be destroyed.

Consider the potential damage caused by the Asian psyllid beetle. It carries a fungus that could destroy California or Florida's entire citrus crop. Losses would be in billions of dollars.

PEST AND DISEASE

Lecture Contents (*continued*)

Disease (*continued*)

Millions of acres of Rocky Mountain pine forests are devastated by the mountain pine beetle (*Dendroctonus ponderosae*). Again, the beetle doesn't actually kill the tree. It dies instead, from the pathogenic fungus that ensues.

Some plant diseases, like bacterial spot, are caused by wet and warm environments. Like the name implies, bacterial spot leaves dark, raised spots on the leaves. Remedy: destroy infected plants. Other common diseases are caused by cool, wet weather, such as bacterial blight. It leaves large, yellow spots on leaves, which eventually turn brown. Remedy: destroy infected plants.

Bacteria Versus Plants

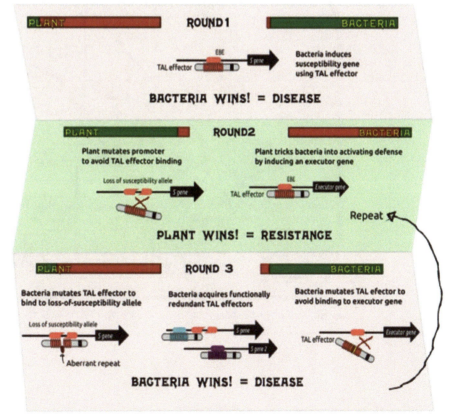

Source: https://openi.nlm.nih.gov/detailedresult.php?img=PMC4500901_fpls-06-00535-g002&req=4.

PEST AND DISEASE

Lecture Contents *(continued)*

Disease *(continued)*

Unlike many human diseases, plant diseases lack cures. As illustrated earlier, most often, infected plants must be destroyed. Thus, successful plant stewardship requires knowledge of disease conditions and strategies to avoid or prevent them. Using disease-resistant plant varieties can be critical to garden and urban tree canopy health and productivity. Proper spacing alleviates disease by contact (or water splash from rain or irrigation). Crop rotation also helps alleviate the buildup of pathogens.

Plant's Resistance to Disease

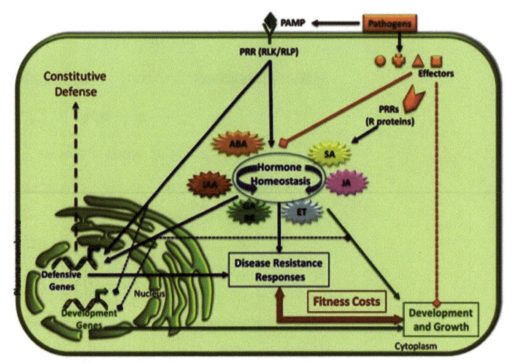

Source: https://openi.nlm.nih.gov/detailedresult.php?img=PMC3662895_fpls-04-00155-g002&req=4.

PEST AND DISEASE

Relevant Links

TEDTalk

Natural Pest Control

https://www.ted.com/talks/shimon_steinberg_natural_pest_control_using_bugs?utm_campaign=tedspread&utm_medium=referral&utm_source=tedcomshare

How Butterflies Self-Medicate

https://www.ted.com/talks/jaap_de_roode_how_butterflies_self_medicate?utm_campaign=tedspread&utm_medium=referral&utm_source=tedcomshare

Wiki (Reference purpose only)

Integrated Pest Management (IPM)   https://en.wikipedia.org/wiki/Integrated_pest_management

Pest Control   https://en.wikipedia.org/wiki/Pest_control

Plant Disease   https://en.wikipedia.org/wiki/Plant_pathology

Others

Environmental Protection Agency

https://www.epa.gov/pesticides

https://www.epa.gov/managing-pests-schools/introduction-integrated-pest-management

Quizzes

© Davidovka/Shutterstock.
com

1. Describe briefly integrated pest management.

2. What evidence do chewing pests leave? What evidence do sucking pests leave?

3. Briefly describe the difference between bacteria, fungi, and virus.

PLANT COMMUNITIES—NATIVE, EXOTIC, INVASIVE

Relevant Words

Biodiversity, Biomimicry, Ecoregion, Exotic plants, *Genius Loci*, Invasive plants, Lawn alternative, Native plants, World Wildlife Federation (WWF)

Lab Objective

To research and identify three common plants for each plant community—native, exotic, and invasive. To describe the benefit from replacing exotic/invasive plants with native plants.

Lab Assignment

- Visit a local nursery.
- Identify three most common nonnative plants sold.
- Research native plants that may be suitable to replace three nonnative plants identified.
- Describe the benefits from the replacement with native plants.

Lecture Outlines

© Andi Muhammad Hasbi
H/Shutterstock.com

- ❖ Exotic Plants
- ❖ Invasive Plants
- ❖ Native Plants and Native Friendly Plants
- ❖ Benefits From Native Plants for Being Sustainable

PLANT COMMUNITIES— NATIVE, EXOTIC, INVASIVE

Lecture Contents

In this chapter, we will discuss native plants, exotic plants, and those termed invasive. It is intended that students of sustainable horticulture will gain an appreciation of where plants come from. Knowing where a plant comes from aids a great deal in knowing care requirements of the plant. Is the new plant intended for your garden from a region with deep, highly fertile soil or from a pine forest with acid soil? Is it from wet cold northern climes or a southern desert? An understanding of where plants come from and how they managed to get to our gardens, urban farms, and landscapes also aids one's quest for interacting with nature. Again, we think it is important to know your plants. It helps you to respect where you dwell.

Six billion years ago, the earth was a fiery ball of molten lava, gas, and hot rocks. It eventually (and rather "recently") would come to be covered by plants. Mosses were the first land plants and appeared on the earth around 470 million years ago. Higher plants (those with water-conducting tissue) evolved around 400 million years ago, and fossils indicate trees existed at 385 million years past. Dinosaurs roamed the planet 243 million years ago—until their extinction 177 million years later, and flowers appeared around 130 million years ago (in contrast, our human ancestors appeared five to seven million years ago).

There have been at least five major ice ages in the earth's history. The most recent glacial advance started 110,000 years ago and ended about 15,000 years ago. We are presently in an interglacial period.

Except for recently developed strains and hybrids, the plants we see today have been adapting in their place of origin since. They are spread across the earth in complex patterns of plant communities called "ecoregions." The World Wildlife Federation (WWF) defines an ecoregion as a "large unit of land or water containing a geographically distinct assemblage of species, natural communities, and environmental conditions." These patterns are determined by climate, geology, and the evolution of their own ability to thrive.

There are 14 distinct ecoregions on the planet, from mangrove forests by the sea to the alpine meadows of the Himalayas (https://www.worldwildlife.org/biome-categories/terrestrial-ecoregions).

PLANT COMMUNITIES—
NATIVE, EXOTIC, INVASIVE

Lecture Contents (*continued*)

© Rvector/Shutterstock.
com

Ecoregion

Deserts and xeric shrublands vary greatly in the amount of annual rainfall they receive; some as much as 10 in. annually, others with 4 in. or less. In desert and xeric shrublands, evaporation exceeds precipitation. Temperature variability is also extremely diverse. Some desert and xeric shrubland ecoregions are hot year-round but others become quite cold in winter. Temperature extremes of heat by day and cold at night are also characteristic.

Tropical and subtropical moist broadleaf forests are found in large, discontinuous patches centered on the equatorial belt. These ecoregions are characterized by low variability in annual temperature and high levels of rainfall (greater than 80 in. per 200 cm annually).

Tropical and subtropical dry broadleaf forests are found in southern Mexico, southeastern Africa, central India, central Brazil, the Caribbean, valleys of the northern Andes, and along the coasts of Ecuador and Peru. These ecoregions are characterized by warm temperature year-round and ample rain. However, they have seasonal droughts that last several months.

Tropical and subtropical coniferous forests are found predominantly in North and Central America. These tropical regions experience low levels of precipitation and moderate variability in temperature. Mexico harbors the world's richest and most complex subtropical coniferous forests.

Temperate broadleaf and mixed forests experience a wide range of variability in temperature and precipitation. In regions where rainfall is broadly distributed throughout the year, deciduous trees mix with species of evergreens. Species such as oak (*Quercus spp.)*, beech (*Fagus spp.*), birch (*Betupa spp.*), and maple (*Acer spp.*) typify the composition of the temperate broadleaf and mixed forests (TBMF).

Temperate evergreen forests are found predominantly in areas with warm summers and cool winters, and vary enormously in their kinds of plant life. In some, needleleaf trees dominate, while others are home primarily to broadleaf evergreen trees or a mix of both tree types. Temperate evergreen forests are common in the coastal areas of regions that have mild winters and heavy rainfall, or inland in drier climates or montane areas. Many species of trees inhabit these forests including pine, cedar, fir, and redwood. The understory also contains a wide variety of herbaceous and shrub species. Temperate evergreen forests sustain the highest levels of biomass in any terrestrial ecosystem and are notable for trees of massive proportions, such as California's coast redwood (*Sequoia sempervirens*) and spruce.

PLANT COMMUNITIES— NATIVE, EXOTIC, INVASIVE

Lecture Contents (*continued*)

Ecoregion (*continued*)

Boreal forests are northern forests, covering most of inland Canada and Alaska; most of Sweden, Finland, and inland Norway; much of Russia; and the northern parts of Kazakhstan, Mongolia, and Japan. Low annual temperatures characterize these northerly latitudes. Precipitation ranges from 15 to 40 in. per year and may fall mainly as snow. The boreal represents 29% of the world's forest cover.

Tropical and subtropical grasslands, savannas, and shrublands. Large expanses of land in the tropics do not receive enough rainfall to support extensive tree cover. The tropical and subtropical grasslands, savannas, and shrublands are characterized by rainfall levels between 90 and 150 cm per year

Temperate grasslands, savannas, and shrublands. Known as prairies in North America, pampas in South America, veld in Southern Africa, and steppe in Asia, temperate grasslands, savannas, and shrublands differ largely from tropical grasslands in the annual temperature regime as well as the types of species found here. Generally speaking, these regions are devoid of trees, except for riparian or gallery forests associated with streams and rivers.

Flooded grasslands and savannas. The everglades are the world's largest rainfed flooded grassland that features 11,000 species of seed-bearing plants.

Montane grasslands and shrublands. This major habitat type includes high-elevation (montane and alpine) grasslands and shrublands. There are tropical, subtropical, and temperate montane grasslands and shrublands. The plants of montane grasslands and shrublands display adaptations to cool, wet conditions and intense sunlight, including features such as rosette structures, waxy surfaces, and abundant pilosity (covered with hairs).

Tundra. The tundra is a treeless polar desert found in the high latitudes in the polar regions, primarily in Alaska, Canada, Russia, Greenland, Iceland, and Scandinavia, as well as sub-Antarctic islands. The region's long, dry winters feature months of total darkness and extremely frigid temperatures. Most precipitation falls in the form of snow during the winter while soils tend to be acidic and saturated with water where not frozen. The tundra supports a limited plant community of sedges, heaths, and dwarf shrubs.

Mediterranean forests, woodlands, and scrub ecoregions are characterized by hot and dry summers, while winters tend to be cool and moist. Most precipitation arrives during these months.

PLANT COMMUNITIES—NATIVE, EXOTIC, INVASIVE

Lecture Contents (continued)

Ecoregion (continued)

Only five regions in the world experience these conditions: the Mediterranean, south-central and southwestern Australia, the fynbos of southern Africa, the Chilean Matorral, and the Mediterranean ecoregions of California. Although the habitat is globally rare, it features an extraordinary biodiversity of uniquely adapted animal and plant species, which can adapt to the stressful conditions of long, hot summers with little rain. Most plants are fire adapted, and dependent on this disturbance for their persistence.

Mangroves occur in the waterlogged, salty soils of sheltered tropical and subtropical shores. They are subject to the twice-daily ebb and flow of tides, fortnightly spring and neap tides, and seasonal weather fluctuations. They stretch from the intertidal zone up to the high-tide mark. These forests are composed of 12 genera comprising about 60 species of salt-tolerant trees.

© display intermaya/
Shutterstock.com

Native Plants

A native plant is one found in its native habitat or grown and planted in its native locale. Because they are kept where they came from, they are resilient in that particular environment. They have adapted to the soil biology. They have adapted to soil chemistry. They have adapted to the climatic conditions. They have adapted to the population of pests at hand, and to other plants in the plant community. In general, they are well-adapted plants. Hence, they play a critical role in sustainable horticulture.

Because native plants thrive under natural conditions to which they have adapted, fewer climate change inputs need to be administered. There will be far less need, if any, for input of synthetic pesticides and fertilizers, for example. Because they are adapted to regional climatic conditions, they usually will not need supplemental irrigation (once established). Hence, they save water. The use of native plants is a form of biomimicry. It is gardening in harmony with the natural environment.

The use of native plants is also said to increase a person's "sense of place." Colorado-native plants in a Colorado garden make it seem like Colorado. Michigan-native plants in a Michigan garden make Michigan gardens "feel" like Michigan, and so forth. A sense of place helps us connect to nature in our place of reside. It helps us respect where we dwell.

Native plants are especially well suited for use in a garden where they are native to, and ought to be considered as a lawn alternative.

PLANT COMMUNITIES— NATIVE, EXOTIC, INVASIVE

Lecture Contents (*continued*)

Native Plants (*continued*)

There are approximately 40 million acres of lawn in the United States. Kentucky bluegrass (*Poa pratensis*) is the most popular lawn in the United States, but it is not native to Kentucky or anywhere in North America. It is native to Europe, Northern Asia, and the mountains of Algeria and Morocco. St. Augustine grass (*Stenotaphrum secundatum*) and Bermuda grass (*Cynodon dactylon*) are popular turf grasses in the arid southwest. They are native to South America and the Mediterranean, respectively.

Unfortunately, turf grasses are rated as "high" with respect to water usage. It varies by species and climate conditions of course, but turf grass can consume as much as 35 to 55 gallons of water per square foot annually. That is a great deal of water!

Adding insult to injury, 900 million pounds of chemicals are applied to these lawns annually as well, according to the Environmental Protection Agency (EPA). These chemicals include toxic herbicides, fungicides, insecticides, and synthetic fertilizers. Lawns are not high on the list of sustainable practices.

Gravel and synthetic turfs, however, are not the answer. Both contribute to the "heat-island-effect"; synthetic turf being even hotter. There are irrigation products on the market to wash and cool fields of synthetic turf. Synthetic turf has an average life of 10 to 12 years, but degrades over time, depending on foot traffic and use. Unfortunately, synthetic turf is not compostable. It must be unloaded at a landfill. Consider plants that are native to your ecoregion instead.

© Samiran Sarkar/
Shutterstock.com

Exotic Plants

Plants that are imported, exported, or grown and used outside any of their native locale described earlier, are called exotics. Exotic species have been a significant source of enjoyment by horticulturalists and plant enthusiasts for thousands of years. The stately iris and beautiful lilies in your garden initially came from a high alpine meadow on the north China border. They are native to China, but we refer to them as exotics at other parts of the globe. Plant explorers and world traveling horticulturalists brought back seeds, bulbs, and specimens long ago.

PLANT COMMUNITIES— NATIVE, EXOTIC, INVASIVE

Lecture Contents (*continued*)

Exotic Plants (*continued*)

It is true that plants from one ecoregion will grow in another ecoregion. But should they? Ethic and ecosystem compatibility questions abound. If you live in a Mediterranean scrub ecoregion, such as Southern California, plant species from other Mediterranean scrub ecoregions may indeed be appropriate. French lavender (*Lavandula dentata*) thrives in Southern California. But plants from a tropical and subtropical moist broadleaf forest, while popular, may not be appropriate there. The large leafed plants require a significant amount of supplemental irrigation when outside their native habitat. Do they pose a threat to functioning ecosystems outside their native range? In some cases, yes; absolutely so.

© Aniko Gerendi Enderle/ Shutterstock.com

Invasive Plants

Exotic species that spread aggressively outside of their boundaries cause economic loss, and are harmful to native habitat are called invasive species. Invasive plants are exotic plants that have "*escaped.*" Invasive plants can change soil chemistry and interfere (quite drastically) in native ecosystem habitat. The examples are almost too numerous to mention here. Invasive species seldom provide food value for native wildlife, and alter the food web in an ecosystem by destroying or replacing native food sources. Experts note invasive plants for contributing to an increased frequency and severity of wildfire.

A plant that is native in one place can be considered an invasive species elsewhere. The California poppy (*Eschscholzia californica*) is the prized state flower for the state of California. Yet is considered a pest in Australia, being listed as an invasive species there. Cold temperatures and snow keep many potential invasive plants under control. What might be considered an invasive plant in California is not an invasive plant in Idaho because of the cold weather. However, with climate change, changes in rain and snow patterns will disrupt this natural protection. Invasive species will gain new territory.

PLANT COMMUNITIES— NATIVE, EXOTIC, INVASIVE

Relevant Links

TEDTalk

A walk on the wild side: 7 Fascinating
experiments in rewilding

https://blog.ted.com/a-walk-on-the-wild-side-7-fascinating-experiments-in-rewilding/

What is it about bees?

https://blog.ted.com/what-is-it-about-bees-three-experts-discuss-why-theyre-fascinating-why-theyre-dying-and-what-can-save-them/

Wiki

Native Plant

https://en.wikipedia.org/wiki/Native_plant

Invasive Species

https://en.wikipedia.org/wiki/Invasive_species

Others

CalFlora

http://calflora.org

California Invasive Plant Council

https://www.cal-ipc.org/plants/inventory/

California Dept. of Food and Agriculture

https://www.cdfa.ca.gov/plant/ipc/index.html

California Native Plant Society

https://www.cnps.org

University of California Division of
Agriculture and Natural Resources

http://ucanr.edu

U.S. Dept. of Transportation –
What is Native Plant?

https://www.environment.fhwa.dot.gov/env_topics/ecosystems/roadside_use/vegmgmt_rdsduse5.aspx

PLANT COMMUNITIES— NATIVE, EXOTIC, INVASIVE

Quizzes

© Davidovka/Shutterstock.
com

1. Describe the primary difference between Native plant and Native-friendly one.

2. Describe of examples of negative impacts from invasive plants.

3. Identify 3 categories in Ecoregion, and, briefly describe each category.

CONTAINER PLANTS AND SUCCULENTS

Relevant Words

House plants, Heating, Ventilation, and Air Conditioning (HVAC), Perlite, Pumice, Root rot, Stem cutting, Succulent, Vermiculite, Volatile Organic Compounds (VOCs)

Lab Objective

To research and identify three common indoor container plants and succulents.
To research and describe optimal growing conditions for each plant identified.

Lab Assignment

- Visit a local nursery.
- Identify three most common indoor container plants and succulents sold.
- Describe the optimal growing conditions as well as common mistakes performed for each plant identified.

Lecture Outlines

❖ Container Plants—Indoor and Outdoor
❖ Succulents
❖ Benefits From Container Plants and Succulents

© Ekaterina Kolchenko/
Shutterstock.com

CONTAINER PLANTS AND SUCCULENTS

Lecture Contents

© Denisik11/Shutterstock. com

Container Plants

Container-grown plants are enormously important in the practice of horticulture. They bring the benefits of gardening to people with little or no space for a garden. They are an excellent remedy for poor soil conditions. They allow the myriad of plant benefits to be brought indoors. Rare plants are often conserved in containers. Containers allow for mobility.

In 2014, U.S. horticulture operations sold $13.8 billion in floriculture, nursery, and other specialty crops, an 18% increase since 2009 (https://www.agcensus.usda.gov/ Publications/2012/Online_Resources/Highlights/Horticulture/Census_of_Horticulture_ Highlights.pdf). Most of that is grown, sold, and shipped in containers.

Amazon lists thousands of books on the subject: *Easy Steps to Container Gardening, 250 Container Design Ideas, The Container Plant Bible,* and so on. Since the beginning of horticulture, plants have been grown in pots. Containers come in many sizes and shapes. They are constructed of various materials. With this chapter, we explore the art and science of the container-grown plant.

Construction of a container by hand, machine, or mold starts with the materials selected. Some containers are constructed of cement, providing excellent durability and resistance to freeze, but heavy to move, of course. If mobility is a concern, or weight is an issue, there are fiberglass or plastic pots. Many plants are grown and shipped in plastic pots. A disadvantage of plastic containers is lack of "breathability."

Cast iron containers are an option as are previously used oak barrels cut in half. Ceramic products range from earthen terra cotta to glazed ceramic, and fine porcelains. Sheet metal, galvanized steel buckets, horse troughs, and tubs can all be used. The key requirement is good drainage. All containers must have at least one drain hole to prevent waterlogged roots and resultant root rot. Containers should be elevated as well to allow for the drain hole(s) to work. Following image shows the use of ceramic "pot feet" to allow for increased drainage.

Container size and container shape are important considerations. It is best to grow a plant in a size where the roots have room to grow, but that is not too spacious. If too spacious, plants can be waterlogged and subject to root rot as there is too much wet soil for the roots to absorb. Water can get stagnant. Certain species do best when their roots are slightly confined. When plants grow, it is necessary to replant them in a larger pot. Thus, shape becomes important. If you plant a tree in a pot that has a large base but narrower top, then the tree cannot be withdrawn without breaking the pot.

CONTAINER PLANTS AND SUCCULENTS

Lecture Contents (*continued*)

Container Plants (*continued*)

Source: Robert Farnsworth

Containers allow for mobility. This is a key benefit of using containers in cooler climates. Plants like tender succulents can be moved indoors when temperatures are below 40°F in fall or winter. Plants are grown in lightweight plastic containers for ease of shipping to nursery, delivery, or final point of sale.

Containers are aesthetic and can be an important feature in a garden. The color, size, shape, texture, and construction material are exciting contributions to a design. The container's surface color (its patina) may change over time due to exposure to the elements. Containers can be used to frame a view or screen a view. They can add seasonal color. They allow for an opportunity to mix plants with different water requirements in the same garden setting. A fine-textured plant with high water requirement can be placed adjacent to a course-textured plant with low water requirement if they are in separate pots (and are watered by hand).

Containers can be a remedy for poor soil conditions. If your planned garden is heavy in clay, an organic loam potting mix can be applied in a container instead. If you live among soils that are acidic or alkaline, a neutral potting mix can be utilized. Compacted soil is also thus remedied. Advantages of containers include their role in bringing plant life and nature to places without soil, such as window box, patio, and rooftop gardens.

CONTAINER PLANTS AND SUCCULENTS

Lecture Contents (*continued*)

Container Plants (*continued*)

Containers, particularly if tall enough, can offer protection from pests. Gophers cannot penetrate the bottom of the container. Rabbits can't climb. Containers can contain a plant with aggressive roots like bamboo (needs a sturdy pot).

Houseplants play an important role in human well-being and would not be possible without containers. In addition to the beauty they bring indoors, research shows that houseplants are quite effective at removing indoor air pollutants. The technology of using houseplant leaves for reducing Volatile Organic C ompounds (VOCs) inside closed facilities has been studied at length and demonstrated by NASA. Philodendrons are effective at removing formaldehyde and benzene. The leaves of golden pothos (*Scindapsus aureus*) have also demonstrated their ability to remove benzene and carbon monoxide from closed chambers.

In 1973, NASA scientists identified 107 VOCs in the air inside the Skylab space station. Synthetic materials, like those used to construct Skylab, give off low levels of chemicals. This effect, known as off-gassing, spreads the VOCs, such as formaldehyde, benzene, and trichloroethylene, all known irritants and potential carcinogens. When these chemicals are trapped without circulation, as was the case on board the International Space Station (ISS), the inhabitants may become ill, as the air they breathe is not given the natural scrubbing by Earth's complex ecosystems.

B.C. Bill Wolverton was an environmental scientist working with the U.S. military to clean up the environmental messes left by biological warfare centers in the 1960s. He led the effort to study this cleansing/remediative effect for NASA. In 1997, he published a book titled *How to Grow Fresh Air: 50 Houseplants That Purify Your Home or Office.* In it, he explains, how plants emit water vapor that creates a pumping action to pull contaminated air down around a plant's roots, where it is then converted into food for the plant. The book lists which plants and varieties remove the most toxins. It has been printed in 12 languages (https://spinoff.nasa.gov/Spinoff2007/ps_3.html).

Houseplants face several unique exposures compared to their outdoor counterparts. Heating, Ventilation, and Air Conditioning systems (commonly referred to as HVAC) can stress plants with artificial spikes of heat or chill. Houseplants don't have the same strength of stem built up over time as their outdoor counterparts, and can be subject to injury by drafts or wind.

CONTAINER PLANTS AND SUCCULENTS

Lecture Contents (*continued*)

Container Plants (*continued*)

Light intensity is far reduced indoors, even at bright windows. The exposure is often closer to "low light" than bright. Most houseplants therefor are usually specimens from the understory of tropical and subtropical jungles. Christmas and Thanksgiving cacti (*Schlumbergera spp.*), for example, originate in warm, shady, and humid tropics.

Water quality for indoor plants is a factor to consider. Unlike rainwater, tap water usually has chlorine in it, which can cause tip burn on a plant. Allowing plant water to sit in an open bucket overnight will allow much of the chlorine to escape. Plants absolutely mustn't be watered through a water softener system, as the water will have an increased concentration of salt. The sodium interferes with the water balance in a plant and can kill them by "fooling" them into thinking they have taken up more water than they have. Softened water essentially causes plants watered with it to die of thirst (https://www.gardeningknowhow.com/plant-problems/environmental/softened-water-and-plants.htm).

Leaves and other organic matter do not normally accumulate in the indoor setting and there are no earthworms or other macroorganisms tunneling through. This creates a different soil system as well. That is why potting mix is recommended instead of a garden mix. The potting mix will have pumice or perlite added (to promote airspace that earthworms might otherwise make) and organic matter and/or vermiculite to help the mix retain moisture.

© Arkadivna/Shutterstock.com

Succulents

Succulents are plants that store water in their leaves, stems, and roots. Because they are adapted to store water, their roots are not as active in foraging for water. Hence the roots are seldom deep or widespread; they can be confined to small spaces, and hence make excellent container specimens.

Most succulents prefer temperatures in the range 40°F to 80°F. While succulents are found on every continent (except Antarctica), they are generally considered too tender for cold climates, and do not fare well in all day scorching sun. Most succulents that we enjoy as nursery stock are from Africa, Central America, South America, and South Africa.

Although all cacti are succulents, not all succulents are cacti. They are considered to be drought tolerant, but not for prolonged periods. They are not plants that do not need water . . . they are plants that store water for later use. With that said, it should be noted that overwatering

CONTAINER PLANTS AND SUCCULENTS

Lecture Contents (continued)

Succulents (continued)

is the leading cause of houseplant failure including succulents. They like to go dry between watering, and should be scheduled for infrequent watering. Succulents like bright light, but contrary to popular belief, most do not fare well with full sun exposure, preferring morning sun and dappled shade instead.

Fertilization requirements are minimal. Succulents don't require fertilizer during winter. Fertilize when they're actively growing in spring, and stop early so they have a chance to use up what's in the soil. As with any houseplant, size at maturity should be considered. Some succulents can get quite large but create an interesting focal point in an entryway. They are easy to maintain with little to no pruning or fuss.

Succulents are quite easy to propagate by stem cuttings. When they become leggy, it is recommended and beneficial to take 3-in. cuttings and replant them for renewed vibrancy. Remove any leaves along the part of the stem to be discarded and save them separately. In order to avoid rot, it is recommended to let the wounds of a succulent cutting callous over prior to initiating root development. Allowing them to dry 3 to 4 days after cuttings are taken should be sufficient.

Once the stem has calloused, rest a cutting on the rim of a jar of water, with the end of the stem just above the surface of the water. Place in a bright location. Adventitious roots will sprout toward the water, but will remain free of "wet feet." When the new roots reach 1 in. in length, it is ready to be replanted in a succulent potting mix.

Allow any succulent leaves that may have fallen to dry for a few days as well. They are easily propagated. Let them lie on top of a tray filled with a cactus/succulent soil mix. Mist lightly approximately once a week until adventitious roots appear. Then gently plant the new roots and begin to water once a week in lieu misting. Avoid overwatering. Allow your propagated succulents to take root, then they can be replanted as desired. Avoid placing them in direct sun until the plants are established.

Many species of succulents will produce offsets, which can be removed by hand and/or sharp knife, and be allowed to callous over. After 3 to 4 days, the calloused offset can be placed into a mix of sand or perlite. Keep it misted once a week until roots appear and then replant in a cactus/succulent potting media.

Succulents are noted for exquisite shapes, texture, and color, which make contrasts, compliments, and combinations endless. Fibonacci's sequence is clearly exhibited in

CONTAINER PLANTS AND SUCCULENTS

Lecture Contents (*continued*)

Succulents (*continued*)

the precise spirals of leaf arrangement. Their flowers are quite stunning. That they are easy to propagate and easy to care for makes succulents a welcome addition in many diverse container garden arrangements for the home and landscape garden.

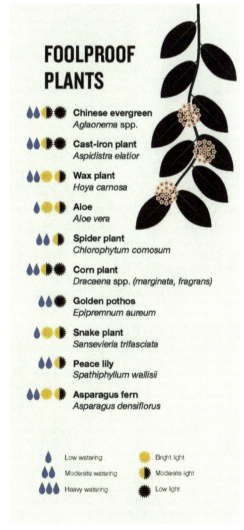

Source: usbg.gov, https://www.usbg.gov/youcangrowit.

CONTAINER PLANTS AND SUCCULENTS

Relevant Links

TEDTalk

How to Grow Fresh Air
https://www.ted.com/talks/kamal_meattle_on_how_to_grow_your_own_fresh_air?utm_campaign=tedspread&utm_medium=referral&utm_source=tedcomshare

How We Can Make Crops Survive Without Water
https://www.ted.com/talks/jill_farrant_how_we_can_make_crops_survive_without_water?utm_campaign=tedspread&utm_medium=referral&utm_source=tedcomshare

Wiki (Reference purpose only)

House Plant
https://en.wikipedia.org/wiki/Houseplant

Succulent Plant
https://en.wikipedia.org/wiki/Succulent_plant

Container Garden
https://en.wikipedia.org/wiki/Container_garden

Others

Indoor Plant Care
https://www.purdue.edu/hla/sites/yardandgarden/wp-content/uploads/sites/2/2016/10/HO-39.pdf

Container Gardening
https://agriculture.wv.gov/divisions/comm/Documents/Publications%20Print/Container%20Gardening%20FINAL%20book.pdf

California Friendly Guide to Native and Drought-Tolerant Gardens
http://www.grandterrace-ca.gov/uploads/8/1/1/9/8119166/a_california-friendly_guide_to_native_and_drought_tolerant_gardens.pdf

CONTAINER PLANTS AND SUCCULENTS

Quizzes

1. Describe the primary benefits of container plants.

2. Describe the unique characteristics of succulents.

3. What is the most common mistake made with container plants?

VEGETABLE AND FRUIT

Relevant Words

Antioxidant, Chill hours, Community-supported agriculture (CSA), Cool-season vegetable, Cruciferous vegetable, Frost damage, Integrated pest management (IPM), Leguminous crop, Olericulture, Pomology, United States Department of Agriculture (USDA) plant hardiness zone map, Warm-season vegetable

Lab Objective

- To research and identify three common vegetables, herbs, and fruit trees.
- To research and describe optimal growing conditions for each plant identified.
- To research and describe growing conditions identified to be more sustainable.

Lab Assignment

- Visit a local nursery.
- Identify three most common vegetables, herbs, and fruit trees sold.
- Research the best growing conditions for plants identified.
- Identify the conditions that may not be sustainable.
- Research possible mitigating method to make more sustainable.

Lecture Outlines

© Libellule/Shutterstock.com

- ❖ Classifications of Vegetables by Part Eaten
- ❖ Sustainable Vegetable Garden
- ❖ Cool Season Versus Warm Season
- ❖ Importance of Fruit Tree Selection
- ❖ Small Fruit Garden

VEGETABLE AND FRUIT

Lecture Contents

© Libellule/Shutterstock.com

Vegetables and Fruits

Olericulture is the branch of horticulture concerning the growth and production of vegetables. *Pomology* is a branch that includes the production and management of fruits. Both are discussed in this chapter. Vegetables and fruits as nutrition are a huge part of human existence and well-being of course, and have been, since our first humanoid ancestors roamed.

Growing our own food allows for security and trust. The United States has banned hundreds of chemicals in this country. Are they used in others? Growing at home or in a community garden assures us that harsh chemicals are not applied. It also lowers the carbon footprint associated with transit and shipping of our food goods across the globe. *The average carrot travels over 1,600 miles to be delivered from farm to table.* China produces half of the world's apples and half of the world's peaches.

There is a process for planning, design, construction, and management of gardens that follow ecological principles. First, check for a sunny location. Fruits and vegetables require full sun (8 hours per day). Make sure to choose a location with an adequate number of frost free days to allow for needed "days to maturity."

Next, evaluate the water supply. While it depends on site-specific exposures such as soils, climate, species, and evapotranspiration rates, growing fruits and vegetables requires water in quantities of about 1 in. per week during the growing season. In many locales, irrigation is required to supplement natural precipitation. There are ways to save water in a garden, but, except for a few rare exceptions, fruits and vegetables are not drought tolerant. Rain water harvest, grey water use, and other water-saving strategies are considered in Chapter 14.

If you have the sunlight and have conceived of other ways to save water, the next step is to evaluate the soil. Fruits (especially stone fruits) and vegetables require excellent drainage, loose soil, and prefer a neutral pH. Abundant organic matter in soil texture and moisture-holding capacity, and supplies much of the needed plant nutrition. If the soil for your planned garden area is of clay content, consider raised beds instead.

Growing fruits and vegetables requires an examination of climatic needs. There are cool-season vegetables (those that thrive at 55°F–65°F) and there are warm-season

VEGETABLE AND FRUIT

Lecture Contents *(continued)*

Vegetables and Fruits *(continued)*

varieties (those that thrive at 65°F–90°F). Cool-season vegetables are usually leafy, such as cabbage, lettuce, and spinach. Warm-season vegetables are those laden with fruit (horticulturally speaking), such as corn, tomatoes, peppers, and pumpkins. It is important to grow in the appropriate season of course.

Growing fruit trees also requires a consideration of climate. First, check the United States Department of Agriculture (USDA) Plant Hardiness Zone Map. Will the species survive the winter? Bartlett pear (*Pyrus communis 'Bartlett'*) is one of the hardier fruit trees and can handle Zones 4 to 7. Zone 4 gets as cold as –30°F (there are a few species that can even handle Zone 3). Apple trees (*Malus spp.*), apricots (*Prunus armeniaca*), and tart cherries (*Prunus cerasus*) are hardy as well. Sweet cherries (*Prunus avium*), plums (*Prunus domestica)*, and peaches and nectarines (*Prunus persica*) require warmer zones.

You must also check to see whether it is cold *enough*. Many fruit trees require "chill hours." Chill hours are consecutive annual hours that a fruit tree spends in temperatures ranging from 45°F to 32°F. Some fruit tree chill hour requirements are as low as 50 (hours). Some require 1,000. The need that these be consecutive is to allow for dormancy. Trees that can adapt to cold temperatures do so by going dormant in the winter. As nights get cooler, and daylight shortens, deciduous fruit trees shed their leaves. Energy production drops. The plant rests until gradually warming in the spring.

Frost damage is also a consideration. Fruit trees that bloom early are susceptible to spring frosts. Apricots bloom early. Cherries are next. These blooms are more susceptible to being killed by spring frosts. Plums, pears, peaches, and apples follow. Apples work best for you if you have consistent spring frosts. There are also differences within varieties. For example, McIntosh apples bloom before Rome Beauty (https://extension.psu.edu/home-orchards-why-is-there-no-fruit-on-my-tree).

Growing fruits and vegetables requires maintenance. Vegetable beds require hand weeding and composting. Fruit production requires informed pruning. Both require careful monitoring and management of integrated pest management (IPM) strategies. Both require a regimen of organic nutrients during their growth phase. But, of course, the fruits are worth the labor.

VEGETABLE AND FRUIT

Lecture Contents (*continued*)

Vegetables

© Inspiring/Shutterstock.com

A word of caution: The following descriptions of benefits of vegetables and fruits should not be taken as medical advice. They are intended only as introductions.

Artichokes (*Cynara scolymus*) are not only nutritious and delicious, they are aesthetic in a garden as well with their large gray leaves and thistle-like purple flowers. The plant is somewhat adapted to dry conditions. Although it is the unopened flower that we eat, the petioles and roots are edible as well. Artichoke contains cynarin, which gives it detoxifying qualities. Artichoke is a perennial and will come back strong in climates where it is hardy. Of U.S. artichokes, 100% are produced in California.

Asparagus (*Asparagus officinalis*) also can be an attractive perennial if left to flower and fruit, but we eat the tender shoots, before its leaves emerge. The red berries are toxic, but the shoots are enormously beneficial. The specific epithet officinalis means medicinal. The list of medicinal qualities is too numerous to mention. It is native to most of Europe, Northern Africa, and Western Asia. China is the world's leading producer.

Beans (*Phaseolus spp.*) are a warm-season annual, native to Central America and the Andes regions of South America. When we eat a bean, we are eating a seed from a pod, much like the closely related pea. Most bean plants are vines and thus need support. Native Americans used corn to support their beans.

Beets (*Beta vulgaris*) have several health benefits. They are high in nutrients and vitamins A and C. We eat what is a tap root, but the greens are high in vitamin C, calcium, and iron.

Basil (*Ocimum basilicum*) is an annual herb in northern gardens. It originated in India, and is considered a holy plant. It is abundant around temples. It thrives in summer heat.

Bok Choy (*Brassica rapa 'chinensis'*) is a cool-season vegetable that can withstand a light frost (frost actually increases its sweetness). It is low in calorie but high in calcium and vitamins.

Broccoli, brussel sprouts, cabbage, cauliflower, collard greens, and *kale* are all cultivars of *Brassica oleracea.* Each one is a cool-season crop. They are among the "cruciferous vegetables," (named because the four petaled flowers are shaped like a cross). Cruciferous vegetables are thought to be a digestive stimulant, but can cause stomach aches for people who are sensitive. Broccoli is an Italian word meaning "flowing top of cabbage." We eat the unopened buds of the inflorescence.

VEGETABLE AND FRUIT

Lecture Contents (*continued*)

Vegetables (*continued*)

Carrots (*Daucus carota 'sativus'*) are usually orange, but there are also purple, red, white, and yellow varieties. The most common edible part is the taproot, but the greens are also edible. Carrots, native to Europe, were initially grown for their aromatic leaves and seeds. A carrot is a biennial. If left in the ground, they will produce flowers in their second year. The flowers of carrot are a companion plant in the garden that will attract beneficial wasps. It is suggested that gardeners leave several over the winter. Carrots are tolerant of limited shade.

Cauliflower. See Broccoli (*Brassica oleracea*) for detailed description.

Celery (*Apium graveolens*) is a marshland, cool-season annual, which has been cultivated as a vegetable since antiquity. Celery seed is also used as a spice and its extracts have been used in herbal medicine. California is the top producer. In ancient Rome, it was thought to be an aphrodisiac.

Chard (*Beta vulgaris*) has nutritious green leaves but the stalks vary in color. Native to the Mediterranean, it is gaining in popularity with benefits like spinach (but easier to grow). It is commonly referred to as Swiss chard, because it was discovered by a Swiss botanist in the 1500s. Chard is a cool-season biennial. Seeds are usually sown between June and October, depending on the desired harvesting period. Chard can be harvested while the leaves are young and tender, or after maturity when they are larger and have slightly tougher stems. Harvesting is a continuous process, as most species of chard produce three or more crops. Raw chard is extremely perishable.

Cilantro (*Coriandrum sativum*) is day length sensitive and should be planted from October to February. It is an ancient old-world herb native to vast regions of southern Europe to India. Coriander is the seed of cilantro.

Collard greens are a loose-leafed cabbage cultivar. See *Broccoli* (*Brassica oleracea*) for detailed description.

Corn (*Maize spp.*) is native to the Americas and was developed from a wild grass 7,000 years ago. It is a warm-season annual, and is one of the world's top four food crops (potatoes, rice, wheat, and corn).

VEGETABLE AND FRUIT

Lecture Contents (*continued*)

Vegetables (*continued*)

Cucumber (*Cucumis sativus*) is a warm-season vine crop native to south Asia. It grows up trellises or other supporting frames with thin, spiraling tendrils. The fruit of the cucumber is classified as a pepo.

Dill (*Anethum graveolens*) is of unknown origin, as it grows wild over the entire European continent. It is an annual herb and is said to have calmative qualities. Its leaves and seeds are used as herbs or spices for flavoring food.

Eggplant (*Solanum melongena*) is a warm-season annual in the Solanaceae (tomato) family, native to India. There are numerous health benefits including antioxidants that help prevent cancer, inflammation, and neurological diseases. Initially, they resembled an egg but have been bred longer and sweeter (like corn and carrots).

Garlic (*Allium sativum*) is a powerful and potent medicinal food. It is a natural antiseptic; it prevents cancer, fights infection, and colds. Garlic also decreases diseases associated with aging such as stroke and arthritis.

Kale is crinkly leaved cabbage that does not form a head. It is closer to wild cabbage. See *Broccoli* (*Brassica oleracea*) for detailed description.

Lettuce (*Lactuca sativa*) is produced in five distinct types. Leaf lettuce is the most widely planted. Romaine lettuce has an upright head. Butterhead is a head lettuce with a loose arrangement of leaves. Crisp lettuce (Iceberg) is adapted to northern climates (extremely sensitive to heat as the name implies). And stem lettuce is used more for cooking.

Leeks (*Allium ampeloprasum*) are in the lily family, along with its relatives onion, garlic, scallions, shallots, and chives. Leeks are striking and graceful (like fountains in the garden). They have a pleasing aroma, and, unlike onion, produce no tears. They are native to the Mediterranean area of Egypt. Best grown midsummer through late fall.

Onions (*Allium cepa*) are a hardy bulb. They are said to be powerful antioxidants that reduce the risk of cancer. They help prevent heart disease and reduce high blood pressure. Workers who built the pyramids were fed radish and onion. Gladiators rubbed them on their skin to firm up their muscles. They are toxic to dogs.

Lecture Contents (*continued*)

Vegetables (*continued*)

Peas (*Pisum sativum*) are a cool-season annual. Snap pea pods are cylindrical, and the pods are cooked. Snow pea pods are flat, have thinner walls, and can be eaten raw. The green shoots are also edible. Peas are leguminous crops and thus are nitrogen fixers.

Peppers (*Capsicum spp.*) are another considered to be an aphrodisiac. Peppers are a warm-season annual with aides against disease.

Potatoes (*Solanum tuberosum*) are the world's fourth largest food crop following rice, wheat, and corn. They originated in Peru and Bolivia. China is the world's largest producer. They are a warm-season annual.

Pumpkins (*Cucurbita pepo*) are a cultivar of a squash plant, native to North America. They (like carrots) can tolerate limited shade.

Radish (*Raphanus sativus*) can grow from a seed to a small plant in as little as 3 days (Raphanus means quickly appearing). It is a cool-season annual prized for its spicy taproot.

Rhubarb (*Rheum rhabarbarum*) is a hardy perennial. Although the leaves are toxic, the petiole is highly desirable.

Rutabagas (*Brassica napobrassica*) are a cool-season annual. They originated as a cross between the cabbage and the turnip. We eat the taproot. Sown in summer, and harvested late autumn onward, they can be left in the ground until needed.

Spinach (*Spinacia oleracea*) is a perennial native to central and southwest (SW) Asia. It may survive (through dormancy) over winter. Rich in vitamin C (helps resist colds and infection), vitamin B (helps keep you clam), and disease-fighting mineral, zinc.

Squash (*Cucurbita spp.*) comes from the Native American word *skutasquash*, which means something that can be eaten raw. Summer squash can be eaten in its entirety including rind and seeds. Butternut squash (*Cucurbita moschata* 'Butternut') and zucchini (*Cucurbita pepo*) are examples of summer squash.

VEGETABLE AND FRUIT

Lecture Contents (*continued*)

Vegetables (*continued*)

Winter squash have tough rinds. Their seeds germinate best when the soil temperature is 70°F to 95°F, but they are harvested in September or October, before the danger of heavy frosts. Examples of winter squash include acorn squash, pumpkin, and spaghetti squash (all three *Cucurbita pepo*).

Sweet potato (*Ipomoea batatas*) is an herbaceous perennial vine native to Central and South America. China produces most worldwide. They are filled with the robust antioxidant beta-carotene. They are also rich in fiber and vitamin E (healthy for your skin).

Tomato (*Solanum lycopersicum*) originated in Mexico and Guatemala and has been propagated since 500 BCE. They are high in dietary fiber and are delicious raw or cooked.

Turnips (*Brassica rapa*) were a staple food for the ancient Greeks and Romans. Although we traditionally eat the root, the greens are more nutritious and richer in vitamins. An excellent source of fiber and remedy for weight loss.

Zucchini tastes best when eaten immature. See Squash (*Cucurbita spp.*) for detailed description.

© Vertes Edmond Mihai/
Shutterstock.com

Fruits

Almonds (*Prunus dulcis*) are produced in USDA Zones 7 to 9. They bear fruit in their third or fourth year. It is the seventh largest U.S. food export. California is the leading producer.

Apples (*Malus spp.*) are a deciduous tree that can bear fruit in the first or second year. China is the leading producer. It is the oldest cultivated tree in the world. Its exact origins are unknown. There are 7,500 known cultivars. Apples are highly susceptible to pests and disease.

Apricot (*Prunus armeniaca*) another whose exact origin is uncertain, as there was extensive prehistoric cultivation. Some research indicates apricots may be an alternative treatment for cancer. California produces the near exclusive apricot supply in Zones 5 to 8. They need a limited number of chill hours. Apricot trees are very aesthetic and are available in standard, dwarf, and semidwarf sizes. But because they bloom early, apricot crops are frequently lost to spring frost.

Lecture Contents (*continued*)

Fruits (*continued*)

Avocado (*Persea americana*) is native to Mexico and Central America and is produced in USDA Zones 9 to 11. Avocados are a drupe, which mature on the tree, but ripen off. California produces 95% of the U.S. crop.

Sweet cherries (*Prunus avium*) are produced in Zones 5 to 7. Sour cherries (*Prunus cerasus*) are produced in Zones 4 to 7. Sour cherry trees are smaller, bear earlier, and have fewer disease problems than sweet cherries. Yoshino cherry (*Prunus cerasus × yedoensis*) is another that is delightful in bloom. People travel from all parts of the world to view the spring-time cherry blossoms of this tree in Washington, DC (3,020 of this ornamental variety were gifted to the United States from Japan in 1912).

Citrus (*Citrus spp.*) are evergreen trees grown in USDA zones 9 and 10. Oranges, grapefruits, lemons, limes, and tangerines are all citrus. The flowers are noted for a strong, but pleasant aroma.

Fig (*Ficus carica*) is a deciduous tree of Zones 7 to 10. The plant can tolerate seasonal drought.

Mulberry (*Morus alba*) grows in any USDA zone. Red mulberry is native to eastern North America. The black mulberry is native to Asia. Mulberry leaves are ecologically important as the silk worm is host specific.

Olive trees (*Olea europaea*) need hot summer temps to ripen and thrive in Zones 9 to 10. California is the exclusive U.S. supplier. They transplant easily and are moderate to fast growing.

Peach (*Prunus persica*) and nectarine (*Prunus persica*) are the same species. Although they are regarded as different fruits at the grocery store or fruit stand, the drupe of nectarine is actually a "fuzz-free" mutation of peach. Unlike suggested in its name, *Prunus persica* is a deciduous tree native to northwestern China, not Persia (present-day Iran). Peach trees are short lived; trees tend to decline rapidly after 10 to 12 years, resulting from winter injury and wood rot infection. California leads the nation in peach and nectarine production. Nectarines bloom earlier and are more susceptible to disease than peach. Peaches require heavy fertilization and frequent pruning.

Pear (*Pyrus communis*) is native to central and eastern Europe and SW Asia. It is grown extensively in the northwest United States, thriving best in Zones 5 to 8. They do have

VEGETABLE AND FRUIT

Lecture Contents (*continued*)

Fruits (*continued*)

a chill hour requirement of 350 (Asian varieties) to 800 (European varieties). An ornamental pear (*Pyrus calleryana*) will grow in Zone 9. Perhaps overused, the Callery pear may be soon listed as invasive. Like the avocado, European pears mature on the tree, but ripen off. Asian varieties ripen on the tree and are crisp like apples.

Persimmon (*Diospyros kaki*) is a Zone 6 to 10 deciduous tree native to Asia. It is quite ornamental with fruit being persistent after the leaves have fallen.

Plums (*Prunus domestica*) are of European or Japanese origin. The European plums are excellent for canning or drying (as for prunes). The Japanese red and yellow plum varieties are for eating fresh. They are a decorative landscape tree available in semidwarf and standard.

Pomegranate (*Punica granatum*) is a pome fruit that is in season September to February. It is a drought-tolerant species grown in California, Arizona, and Iran.

The list of vegetables and fruits is extensive, and there are thousands more including in your locale. This chapter was intended as an introduction (https://ucanr.edu/sites/placernevadasmallfarms/files/170644.pdf).

Fruits and vegetables ought to make up half of your plate at any given meal—about 30% vegetables and 20% fruits. A diverse selection of colors adds variety in both flavor and nutrition (https://health.gov/dietaryguidelines/2015/guidelines/).

Fruit and vegetable sales topped $104.7 billion in 2016, in the United States alone. That represents growth of 3.3% since the year before (https://www.grandviewresearch.com/industry-analysis/us-fruit-vegetables-market).

Organic fruits and vegetables are up 8.4% in the United States to a total of 15.6 billion annual (https://www.supermarketnews.com/produce-floral/fruits-and-vegetables-driving-organic-sales-record-heights).

Fruits and vegetables are not only good for you, they are also good for your career. Growing fruits and vegetables is a viable career choice, especially with the growing concern for healthy local food systems and community-supported agriculture (CSA). And if done right, in collaboration with nature and keen stewardship, gardens and urban farms can be beneficial for the local community and personal well-being.

Lecture Contents (*continued*)

Vegetable Types

© ecspelliarmus/
Shutterstock.com

Warm-Season Vegetable

- Daytime temperature 65°F to 90°F and nighttime lows no less than 55°F
- Bean, corn, cucumber, eggplant, pepper, potato, sweet potato, pumpkin, melon, squash, tomato

Cool-Season Vegetable

- Daytime temperature 50°F to 65°F and tolerate the light frost
- Under the warm climate, the early flowering (bolting)—undesirable for vegetable growth
- Artichoke, beet, broccoli, cabbage, carrot, cauliflower, celery, kale, leek, lettuce, green onion, onion, parsnip, pea, radish, spinach, turnip

Vegetable Gardening

Mild Winter Areas

- Possible year-round growing
- Minimal difference between summer and winter temperature—More acceptable for cool-season vegetable
- *Frost-free period*—Important factor in vegetable gardening in the relevance to cultivar selection of warm-season vegetable
- *Days to maturity*—Number of days from sowing or transplant to the harvest
- Fall gardening to extend the growing season—Delaying the planting of cool-season vegetable to have the later harvest

Vegetable Garden Planning

1. Site selectiono
   - ○ Fast draining soil and full sunlight
   - ○ Away from trees and buildings

2. Determining the plot size
   - ○ Typical size for the beginners—25 × 25 ft

Lecture Contents (*continued*)

Vegetable Gardening (*continued*)

3. Garden plot layout
   - Rows running east and west to avoid shades
   - Succession cropping—Continuous harvest throughout the season
   - Intense or blocking gardening—growing vegetable in blocks, not rows (maximum yield from minimum space) / 4- × 4-ft blocks

Vegetable Selection

- Recommended list from the local Cooperative Extension

Soil Preparation

- *Preplanting incorporation*—Weed removal and fertilization to replace nutrients used by the previous crops
- *Residual life*—A short effective period of weed control chemicals: important element to be identified to avoid adversary impact on vegetable

Vegetable Planting

1. Sowing
   - Heavy sowing to ensure a sufficient strand of plants in case of poor germination
   - *Interplanting*—Mixture of slow- and fast-maturing plants to save planting space
   - *Hill planting*—Grouping several plants together
   - To keep the surface of the soil moist after sowing

2. Transplanting
   - To be short, sturdy, and with foliage to the base (to avoid yellowed foliage or bare stems)
   - Overcast day or early evening for transplanting to lessen shock
   - The root ball to be cut shallowly on each side to avoid growing within the original soil ball
   - Transplanting with peat moss—To plant with the pot intact, but top of the pot to be broken down to the soil, avoiding the water wicking from the pea pot
   - To be planted slightly deeper than being grown originally
   - After planting, to be watered with *starter fertilizer*

VEGETABLE AND FRUIT

Lecture Contents (*continued*)

Vegetable Garden Maintenance

1. Thinning
   - Removal of excess seedlings to avoid overdensity
   - Once or twice for each crop
     - One-time thinning: To be done as soon as the leaves of neighboring plants touch each other
     - Twice over thinning: Practical for leaf vegetable, such as chard or lettuce. First time done while seedling, the second time for 2 to 4 weeks later

2. Weeding
   - Pulling, hoeing, or mulching

3. Mulching
   - Layer of plant-derived or synthetic material laid on the soil surface over the roots of plants
   - Reducing weeding and conserving soil moisture
   - In general, 2 in. to 3 in. thick
   - Plastic mulch—Good for accumulating heat underneath the plastic

4. Hot caps
   - Paper or plastic domes set over plants in early spring to hasten the growth

5. Watering
   - To begin as soon as sowing
   - As often as necessary to avoid wilting
   - *Diurnal wilting*—During the hot day due to an inability to absorb enough moisture to compensate for the water loss through the leaves
   - To soak the soil to a depth of about 18 in.

6. Fertilizing
   - To avoid deficiency symptoms
   - Nitrogen can stimulate leaf production at the expense of the vegetable

7. Training
   - To keep the vegetable from becoming dirty or rotten by avoiding the soil contact
   - Teepee training—For cucumber or bean/1-ft interval tying for the vines to the stakes
   - Staking—For tomato or bean

VEGETABLE AND FRUIT

Lecture Contents (*continued*)

Vegetable Garden Maintenance (*continued*)

- ○ String trellis—For bean or pea/10-ft deep pole to provide a sturdy support for the trellis
- ○ Tomato cages—Wire mesh cylinder

Crop Rotation

- Planting of crops in different areas of the garden every year
- Deterrent against the buildup of disease and insects for a particular crop

Cover Cropping

- To maintain fertility in established vegetable garden
- To be planted in fall over the vegetable garden

Green Manure Crops

- To improve poor soil before vegetable planting
- To be planted any time of the year, grown halfway to maturity then turned under to decay
- To sow and wait to grow until 8 to 10 in. high, turn it under, wait 10 to 14 days, then, resow another green manure crop within 3 weeks
- Plowing and resowing repeatedly until the soil is of acceptable quality

© kolopach/Shutterstock.com

Site Selection for Fruit Tree

1. Soil drainage
   - ○ Rapid water drains to allow air to penetrate to the roots
   - ○ Stone fruits (cherry, plum, peach, nectarine) most susceptible to poor drainage

2. Sunlight
   - ○ As much sun as possible—Minimum 6 hours of direct sun per day

VEGETABLE AND FRUIT

Lecture Contents (*continued*)

Site Selection for Fruit Tree (*continued*)

3. Land slope and exposure
   ○ Upper part of slope ideal to avoid the frost
   ○ Southern slopes are best

Tree Crops and Landscape

1. Nut trees for deciduous shade trees
2. Dwarf trees as a screen
3. Dwarf fruit trees as patio trees
4. Espalier fruit trees

Fruit Tree Types

1. Standard—Normal size: 30 ft wide 20 to 25 ft tall (Nut tree)
2. Semidwarf—10 to 15 ft tall
3. Dwarf—5 to 12 ft tall (to be produced by grafting, either rootstock or interstock, and genetic dwarfing)

Fruit Tree Maintenance

1. Watering
   ○ In general, watering deeply every 1 to 2 weeks during the first growing season, then every 3 weeks in subsequent years
   ○ Drip irrigation preferred

2. Fertilization
   ○ Yearly fertilizing
   ○ *Drill-hole* method: Areas covered with grass or groundcover
   ○ *Surface topdressing* method: Typical fruit tree areas

VEGETABLE AND FRUIT

Lecture Contents (*continued*)

Fruit Tree Maintenance (*continued*)

3. Pruning
   - Four main pruning styles
     - Central leader—Used on most of nut trees
     - Modified central leader—Used on apple, pear, plum
     - Vase shape (open center form)—Common on peach, apricot, nectarine
     - Espalier form—For apple, pear

4. Training
   - To create the desired form

5. Fruit thinning
   - Removal of a portion of the small fruits

Failure to Bear Fruits

1. Age

2. Pollination problems
   - Incompatibility of the pollen with the female flower parts
   - Nonviable pollen
   - Failure of the pollen and female flower parts to attain maturity at the same time
   - Dioecious plants

3. Insufficient winter chilling
4. Insufficient sunlight
5. Frost or rain during the pollination period

VEGETABLE AND FRUIT

Lecture Contents (*continued*)

Fruit Tree Forms

Central leader form

Modified central leader form

Vase form

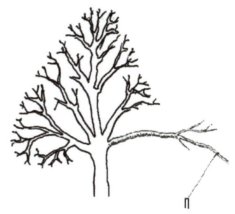

Wide branch crotch to form

Relevant Links

TEDTalk

How We Can Eat Our Landscapes
https://www.ted.com/talks/pam_warhurst_how_we_can_eat_our_landscapes?utm_campaign=tedspread&utm_medium=referral&utm_source=tedcomshare

Grow Your Own Clothes
https://www.ted.com/talks/suzanne_lee_grow_your_own_clothes?utm_campaign=tedspread&utm_medium=referral&utm_source=tedcomshare

A Teacher Growing Green
in the South Bronx
https://www.ted.com/talks/stephen_ritz_a_teacher_growing_green_in_the_south_bronx?utm_campaign=tedspread&utm_medium=referral&utm_source=tedcomshare

A Guerilla Gardener in
South Central LA
https://www.ted.com/talks/ron_finley_a_guerilla_gardener_in_south_central_la?utm_campaign=tedspread&utm_medium=referral&utm_source=tedcomshare

Global Food Waste Scandal
https://www.ted.com/talks/tristram_stuart_the_global_food_waste_scandal?utm_campaign=tedspread&utm_medium=referral&utm_source=tedcomshare

What's Wrong With
What We Eat
https://www.ted.com/talks/mark_bittman_on_what_s_wrong_with_what_we_eat?utm_campaign=tedspread&utm_medium=referral&utm_source=tedcomshare

My Subversive Garden Plot
https://www.ted.com/talks/roger_doiron_my_subversive_garden_plot?utm_campaign=tedspread&utm_medium=referral&utm_source=tedcomshare

Wiki (Reference purpose only)

Vegetable
https://en.wikipedia.org/wiki/Vegetable

Fruit
https://en.wikipedia.org/wiki/Fruit

Others

The California Garden Web
http://cagardenweb.ucanr.edu/Vegetables/

The California Back Yard Orchard
http://homeorchard.ucanr.edu/Fruits_&_Nuts/

Vegetable Research and
Information Center
https://vric.ucdavis.edu

Fruit & Nut Research &
Information Center
http://fruitsandnuts.ucdavis.edu

VEGETABLE AND FRUIT

Quizzes

© davidovka/Shutterstock.
com

1. List three examples of vegetables for each warm season and cool season.

2. _____ is the branch of horticulture concerning the growth and production of vegetables. _____ is a branch that includes the production and management of fruits.

3. Describe at least three primary reasons for the failure of bearing fruits.

PLANTS AND WATER

Relevant Words

California Irrigation Management Information System (CIMIS), Density factors (K_d), Department of Water Resources (DWR), Drip emitter, Drip irrigation system, Estimations of applied water use, Evaporation, Evapotranspiration (ET), Evapotranspiration pan, Gray water, Landscape coefficient (K_L), Landscape coefficient method (LCM), Landscape evapotranspiration (ET_L), Lysimeter, Maximum Applied Water Allowance (MAWA), Microclimate, Microclimate factors (K_{mc}), Precipitation, Rainwater harvesting, Reference evapotranspiration (ET_0), Rotor irrigation system, Runoff, Species factors (K_S), Spray irrigation system, Transpiration, Water Use Classifications of Landscape Species (WUCOLS)

Lab Objective

To research water use requirements of specific ornamental plant species, for realization of optimal plant health, and increased efficiencies in the use of water resources.

Lab Assignment

- Research and identify the water needs for an ornamental plant species.
- Identify a possible water source that may be more sustainable than tap water.
- Research possible methods for collecting and distributing the reusable water.
- Define WUCOLS (**W**ater **U**se **C**lassification **O**f **L**andscape **S**pecies) and landscape coefficient method.

Lecture Outlines

© Incomible/Shutterstock.com

❖ Role of Water for a Plant's Growth
❖ Water Conservation and Reusable Water: Rainwater Harvesting, Gray Water Use, Storm Water Management
❖ Drought-Tolerant Plants and Water-Saving Factors
❖ WUCOLS and Landscape Coefficient Method (LCM)
❖ Evapotranspiration (ET) in California Irrigation Management Information System (CIMIS)

PLANTS AND WATER

Lecture Contents

Plants and Water

Seven billion gallons of water are used on lawns, golf courses, cemetery grounds, and landscapes in the United States daily! According to the Environmental Protection Agency (EPA), half of that amount is lost to evaporation, leaks, runoff, and faulty design. We must start saving water. It is a precious, yet at-peril resource.

We could write volumes on the need to conserve water. We are hopeful instead, that you as a concerned world citizen might already understand such prerequisite. As a sustainably minded horticulturalist, you most certainly have already accepted the fact that this resource ought not to be wasted.

Many join you in this quest to save water, but the answers to our water requirement questions are often vague and confusing. Watering instructions are often listed on the label of a plant at the local retail nursery. If even listed, typical instructions include "Water deeply once established … or Water occasionally … or Prefers moisture. … What do these instructions actually mean?

Unfortunately, most research on plant water requirements to date has been spent on agricultural or timber production crops, but not on ornamental landscape plants and their unique growing conditions. Corn doesn't grow near hot sidewalks and parking lots, for example. Traditionally, we have designed landscapes to be beautiful and complex, and then simply turn the water on, as if it were an unending supply from an invisible source.

But that is not the way of the sustainably minded horticulturalist. It makes sense to estimate a plant's water use requirements closely. Optimal plant health is thus achieved. Plants like it neither too wet nor too dry. Drowning is the leading cause of ornamental plant failure, followed closely by dying of thirst (or drought).

ET is a term applied to the sum of water lost by evaporation from the soil surface and by transpiration from the leaves of the plants combined. If one could calculate the amount of water lost to ET, one could estimate the amount of water that a plant actually needs.

Factors that affect the rate of ET include the amount of solar radiation, atmospheric vapor pressure, temperature, wind, and soil moisture. ET accounts for most of the water lost from the soil during the growth of a crop.

PLANTS AND WATER

Lecture Contents (*continued*)

Plants and Water (*continued*)

If we know how much water is lost from a specific plant or planting, then we know how much water needs to be given back to the specific plant or planting. Estimating ET rates is thus important in planning irrigation schemes.

Several methods are available for estimating a plant's rate of ET. Some involve using specialized devices, such as an evaporation pan or a lysimeter, to measure in the field the components of the overall rate, afterward adding the components together. Others involve calculating the evapotranspiration rate indirectly.

Using one of the indirect methods is the easiest way to proceed, and the result from such a calculation usually is sufficiently accurate for estimating a landscape's irrigation needs.

The most popular indirect approach involves using what's known as the reference evapotranspiration, ET_o. The ET_o is defined as the rate of ET of an extensively studied reference species—one that is well watered, actively growing, and completely shading the soil. In most instances, a short grass, or alfalfa, is used as reference. We apply factors (discussed later) to compare our subject plant(s) to the ET rates of the reference plant. Horticulture scientists developed the concept of ET_o to avoid having to estimate the ET of many different species of plants individually under different sets of conditions.

Landscape evapotranspiration, ET_L, is the maximum average water requirement for plants in a given climate, usually expressed in inches per day. Will gardens you are planning need supplemental water, and if so, how much? Water requirements of ornamental landscape plantings can be determined using the LCM formula as follows:

$$ET_L = K_L \times ET_o$$

Landscape Evapotranspiration = Landscape Coefficient × Reference Evapotranspiration.

With this method, one can estimate water loss from individual plants and/or groups of plants (provided one knows water use characteristics of a species), then calculate how much irrigation water needs to be applied to keep the plant(s) in optimal health.

PLANTS AND WATER

Lecture Contents (*continued*)

Plants and Water (*continued*)

In California, ET_o rates are available through CIMIS. In CIMIS, we can find up to the hour data on factors pertinent to irrigation management, such as recordings of precipitation, solar radiation, vapor pressure, air temperature, relative humidity, wind speed, wind direction, and soil temperature. "CIMIS is a program unit in the Water Use and Efficiency Branch, Division of Statewide Integrated Water Management, California Department of Water Resources (DWR) that manages a network of over 145 automated weather stations in California. CIMIS was developed in 1982 by DWR and the University of California, Davis (UC Davis). It was designed to assist irrigators in managing their water resources more efficiently" (https://cimis.water.ca.gov/).

We find the rate of ET_o in CIMIS, and insert the rate of ET_o into the equation. The number represents measurement in inches.

Then we evaluate factors and conditions specific to the plant(s) in question, and determine the plant's landscape coefficient or K_L. To calculate K_L, the species, density, and microclimate factors must be included:

$$K_L = K_s \times K_d \times K_{mc}$$

Landscape Coefficient = Species Factor × Density Factor × Microclimate Factor.

For this, we reference the WUCOLS manual, developed by L. R. Costello and a few horticulture consultants and instructors at the University of California Cooperative Extension, Half Moon Bay, California. *Ostello and associates* have evaluated several thousand popular landscape plants for their water use needs based on field observation, and began to list those evaluations in a publication called the *Water Use Classifications of Landscape Species (WUCOLS)*. The factors described above are given in ranges.

Species factors range from 0.1 to 0.9 and are divided into four categories, based on their general water needs. A plant with very low water needs is assigned a value of 0.1 or less. A thirsty, water-needing plant is assigned a factor of 0.9.

Very low	<0.1
Low	0.1–0.3
Moderate	0.4–0.6
High	0.7–0.9

PLANTS AND WATER

Lecture Contents (*continued*)

Plants and Water (*continued*)

K_d or density factors range from 0.5 to 1.3. As the density increases in the planting, so does the density factor (if more leaves are present, there are more leaves transpiring, which, in turn, equates to more water lost through ET). The range for density is separated into three categories:

Low	0.5–0.9
Average	1.0
High	1.1–1.3 (lots of diverse plants crowded together)

Plantings that are full but are predominately of one vegetation type are assigned to the average category 1.0.

And finally, one must examine microclimate factors. Microclimates exist in every landscape and need to be considered in estimates of plant water loss. If the microclimate is hot and windy, for example, an increased water use factor is applied. If we locate plants on the east side of a building (with morning sun, but generally more shade), it would warrant a lower microclimate adjustment than if the same plants were planted on the south end of a building. Plants on the south and west sides are subject to longer periods in scorching sun, and would thus be provided a higher microclimate adjustment. Many flower beds will be adjacent to heat-absorbing surfaces such as buildings, walkways, emergency access, parking, and reflective surfaces. The microclimate factor ranges from 0.5 to 1.4, and is divided into three categories:

Low	0.5–0.9
Average	1.0
High	1.1–1.4

With species, density, and microclimate factors inserted into the formula, the resultant landscape coefficient (K_L) is multiplied by the published ET for your vicinity (through CIMIS or other). The result provides us with an estimation of the inches of water needed (per day, per month, or per year). It is easy then to convert inches to gallons, by applying a factor of 0.623.

PLANTS AND WATER

Lecture Contents (*continued*)

Plants and Water (*continued*)

Fortunately, the state of California has taken a leading role in requiring that attention be paid to determining landscape plant water needs. In many jurisdictions, it is increasingly required that estimations of applied water use (EWU) be less than determinations of maximum applied water allowance (MAWA). In California, these are mandated by California State Assembly Bill 325.

In sustainable horticulture, we find what the plants will need instead of simply turning on the water. If practiced by many, we could save billions of gallons, and billions of dollars. And our landscapes can still thrive, with *Genius Loci (Sense of Place)*.

Once water use is estimated, an informed choice of irrigation method should be considered. As discussed in Prologue at the beginning this book, the use of irrigation was first implemented in 3,500 BCE. Current trends have advanced considerably of course, but it was the ancient people who passed on techniques to reduce loss by evaporation and waste. Drip irrigation, for example, is a result of progress from previous attempts with porous clay pots buried in the soil.

Today, in home landscapes, urban farms, and gardens, there are basically four methods of irrigation: by hand, drip, spray, and rotor.

Hand watering should not to be underestimated. It is another measure we can take to connect with our garden and the space where we dwell. It is therapeutic. It allows a close monitoring of your plants for their moisture requirements. Runoff can be easily controlled. It allows for a close monitoring of pests and weed management needs, as well as pleasures of the garden.

Drip irrigation, as the name implies, is an irrigation delivery mechanism where the water is dripped directly to the desired plant by small emitters in an above ground pipe (for drips at the base of the plant) or an underground pipe for drips directly to the roots. The goal is to save water, by delivering it to where it is needed only, thus eliminating waste by runoff, and reducing waste by evaporation.

It is healthy for a garden in that leaves are kept dry (and therefore less likely to be attacked by mold and disease). Diminished growth of weeds is achieved because weed seeds and seedlings are not watered and diminishing growth of weeds (by not watering potential weed seeds with overspray).

PLANTS AND WATER

Lecture Contents (*continued*)

Plants and Water (*continued*)

In addition to those described earlier, an advantage of drip is ease of installation. It is a simple process to lay the drip tubing along the soil toward intended plants. A disadvantage is disruption due to the pipe being accidentally compromised by tripping or shoveling (or even vandalized) when they are not buried at all, or just underneath the surface and/or mulch.

Drip irrigation is often used in drought-tolerant gardens, but there is some doubt about this, as being best practice. Plants that are drought tolerant are usually adapted as such because of wide-spreading roots and/or tap roots of considerable depth. Plant roots forage for water and nutrients. A drip emitter at the base of the plant creates a miniature wetland. The plant roots have no reason to spread and to adapt to drier conditions. Drip works well for plants that need regular and/or ample water and have confined roots by species or by container.

A spray system delivers water (via spray) in a constant flow, for a set amount of time. They can cover full circle, half circle, or quarter circle, and a few other variations. They are a popular choice because they deliver a steady flow. Designed to be installed with "head to head" (overlapping) coverage, they can apply water quickly and uniformly. Quickly and uniformly is a disadvantage on slopes, however, as water runs off faster than it is absorbed.

Unlike spray irrigation, rotors are an irrigation system where water is delivered at intervals, because the nozzle rotates and moves its targeted drops from one position in the garden or landscape to another and back again. Because it gives water a chance to infiltrate before the rotor "returns" to its starting point, there is less runoff, and thus rotors are better suited for slopes. Rotors are often used in larger spaces because of their extended trajectory.

Rainwater Harvesting and Gray Water Use

© Supriya07/Shutterstock.com

Rainwater harvesting is a powerful and simple way to conserve water. A 1,000 sq. ft catchment area (roof/driveway/pavement) yields around 600 gallons of water during a 1-in.rain event. The "*captured*" water can then be used in the landscaped areas, such as garden or urban farm, when needed.

Rainwater harvesting can serve several benefits. Water conservation is primary, and must be of paramount concern. Still, some say that it doesn't rain enough (in the arid south-west) to warrant rainwater harvesting. Some say it doesn't rain enough, therefore, ***we absolutely need to harvest.***

PLANTS AND WATER

Rainwater Harvesting and Gray Water Use (*continued*)

Some cities such as Tucson, Arizona, require rainwater harvesting for landscapes of new buildings and offer rebates toward installation of same. It is encouraged in California as well. Rainwater harvesting is illegal in Colorado, however, as the state wrestles with antiquated western water law.

Rainwater harvesting aids in the reduction of nonsource point pollution. Residue from automobile brake pads, antifreeze from leaky radiators, and leaking engine oil all too often make its way into our surrounding creeks and ultimately large waterways.

Although rainwater itself is clean, the catchment area can easily be contaminated with bird droppings, squirrel and other rodent feces, and blowing dust. Although not a problem when storing rainwater for landscape use, drinking water systems require filtration to meet clean water safety standards.

A simple calculation that converts precipitation (in inches) to gallons of water collectable per square footage of collection surface is as follows:

(Catchment sq. ft) × (Inches Precipitation) × 0.62 = Gallons Collected

This formula works for annual or specific storm calculations. In a location that receives 12 in. of rain annually, for example, a 1,000 sq. ft roof would yield 7,450 gallons annually ($1,000 \times 12 \times 0.62 = 7,450$ gallons). A 0.5-in. rainstorm one February afternoon would yield 310 gallons return to the chosen rainwater catchment ($1,000 \times 0.5 \times 0.62 = 310$ gallons). Examining the distribution of rainfall during the growing season in your region allows you to determine potential tank recharge events (i.e., rainy days).

Gray water is water that has come out of the faucet or other water source one time. Whether used or not, it is considered gray water. Water that goes down the drain while the shower water is heating can be collected instead, and used in the garden as gray water. Plumbing from a sink for handwashing, or vegetable rinsing, or even from a laundry machine can be diverted to the garden, provided organic biodegradable soaps are used.

Water resources are vulnerable to a changing hydrology that is being driven by climate change. The frequency, magnitude, and duration of extreme storm events are changing, which, in turn, affects water quantity, quality, and the infrastructure for stormwater. Warmer temperatures reduce snowpack, which is a critical storage mechanism that slowly releases water used through the year. Warmer temperatures also increase evapotranspiration from plants and evaporation from soils, increasing the need for additional supplemental irrigation for longer periods of the year.

PLANTS AND WATER

Rainwater Harvesting and Gray Water Use (*continued*)

Droughts are likely to become more frequent and last for longer periods during this century. According to the United Nations World Water Development Report 2015, economic losses due to water-related hazards have risen significantly since 1992. Floods, droughts, and storms have affected 4.2 billion people (95% of all people affected by all disasters) and caused US$1.3 trillion of damage (63% of all damage).

An estimated 20% of the world's aquifers are being overexploited, leading to serious consequences such as land subsidence and saltwater intrusion. By 2030, the world is projected to face a 40% global water deficit under the business-as-usual climate scenario. Changes must come (http://www.unesco.org/new/fileadmin/MULTIMEDIA/HQ/SC/images/WWDR2015Facts_Figures_ENG_web.pdf).

Rainwater Harvesting and Gray Water Use (*continued*)

Water Cycle

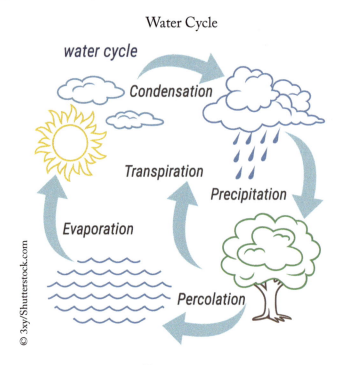

Transpiration

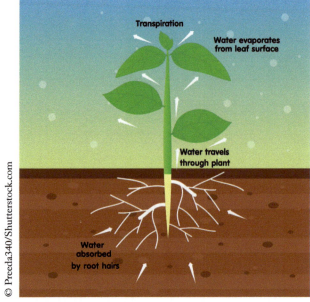

PLANTS AND WATER

Relevant Links

TEDTalk

The Ingenuity of Water Harvesting

https://www.ted.com/talks/anupam_mishra_the_ancient_ingenuity_of_water_harvesting?utm_campaign=tedspread&utm_medium=referral&utm_source=tedcomshare

TEDx—Nanotechnology Will Revolutionize Water Supply Sustainability

http://tedxvirginiatech.com/2012/11/peter-vikesland-at-tedxvt-2012-nanotechnology-will-revolutionize-water-supply-sustainability/

TEDx—The Other Side of Water

https://tedxboston.org/speaker/goodtree

Wiki (Reference purpose only)

Evolutionary History of Plants

https://en.wikipedia.org/wiki/Evolutionary_history_of_plants

Water Resources

https://en.wikipedia.org/wiki/Water_resources

Others

BBC—Why Do Plants Need Water?

https://www.bbc.com/bitesize/clips/ztjd7ty

New York Botanical Garden—Hidden Partners: *Mycorrhizal* Fungi and Plants

http://sciweb.nybg.org/science2/hcol/mycorrhizae.asp.html

Water: Lifeblood of Energy

https://youtu.be/kkqf3WRwquI

Penelope Cruz Is Water

https://www.conservation.org/nature-is-speaking/Pages/Penelope-Cruz-Is-Water.aspx

PLANTS AND WATER

Quizzes

© Davidovka/Shutterstock.
com

1. What does WUCOLS stand for? Describe it briefly and its purpose.

2. Describe three different types of irrigation systems, and identify the most water efficient system and why.

3. What is the formula for converting precipitation to gallons of water collectable per square footage of collection surface?

PRUNING

Relevant Words

Bonsai, Branch collar, Espalier, Hard pruning (aka rejuvenation pruning), Heading back, Lopper, Old wood Versus new wood, One-third rule, Parterre, *Penjing (Penai)*, Pollarding, Pruner, Relief cut, Renewal pruning, Shearing, Topiary

Lab Objective

To observe tree pruning practices and to identify the "Dos and Don'ts" of various pruning methods, and to prepare the proper pruning recommendations for proper pruning.

Lab Assignment

- Explore your neighborhood for pruned tree observation.
- Identify "Good, Bad, and Ugly" examples of tree pruning and describe why.
- Research the proper tree pruning techniques.

Lecture Outlines

❖ Purpose of Pruning: Tree Health Maintenance
❖ Basic Pruning Methods
❖ Timing of Pruning
❖ Knowledge of "*One-Third*" Rule

© solgas/Shutterstock.com

PRUNING

Lecture Contents

Pruning

© provector/Shutterstock.com

Axes are among the first tools ever used. Saws then were first constructed in 5,000 BCE. The art and science of pruning, like horticulture itself, dates back thousands of years.

Pruning has several advantages. It is known to increase productivity, and if done properly, can contribute to overall plant health. Pruning helps maintain plant vigor, and is helpful for flowering and resultant fruits. It can be both hard and grueling work, and it can be therapeutic and restful as well. Pruning a *Bonsai* or *Penjing (aka Penai)*, for example, can be quite calming (and requires no heavy machinery).

Pruning is cutting a shrub, tree, or flower, to take away dead, dying, or diseased parts of the plant. Insect eggs and larvae thrive in decaying matter. Dead wood and dying parts of the plant provide prime habitat, and invite potential pests.

We prune trees for their health. Thinning a dense canopy allows for increased airflow, which helps prevent diseases caused by fungus and bacteria. Thinning also allows increased sunlight penetration, which helps interior leaves and fruit formation. Crossing branches that rub against each other are injured every time the branches are moved by wind. Wounds fester as branches grow thicker and exert increased pressure on the crossing points. Pests and decay are on the scene soon thereafter.

We prune to maintain natural tree form. Erratic branches, suckers, and sprouts all distort the natural habit of the plant. A well-approached prune can highlight a plant's beauty.

We prune to stimulate growth in sparse areas of the tree and restrict growth where too much growth is undesirable. We also prune for aesthetics. *Parterre, espalier,* and *topiary* are pruning methods that have adorned gardens since the Renaissance.

Parterre is based on embroidery, as in the great gardens at Versailles. These gardens were meant to be viewed from above, rather than viewed while strolling through. *Espalier* is pruning a tree, shrub, or vine flat against a wall, wire frame, or trellis. It originated when communities had protective walls (to safeguard against enemy intruders). To feed the village, it was a useful means to produce fruit with limited space. *Topiary* is pruning to whimsical shapes.

Pollarding involves pruning tree branches back to a grotesque and gnarled stub. In days past, it was a useful means to prolong the availability of firewood for fuel. New branches (suckers and water sprouts) would quickly appear, to be harvested again and again

Lecture Contents (*continued*)

Pruning (*continued*)

(cutting the entire tree would eliminate the source). This method of pruning is known as pollarding, and is now routinely done for aesthetics.

We prune for safety. A limb must be removed that otherwise might obscure a stop sign. We might raise the canopy on a tree near parking or entry to assure visibility. We thin a canopy and prune limbs that obscure night lighting over sidewalks. We trim damaged or weak limbs overhanging a playground.

We prune to maintain size, albeit we ought to perhaps choose a plant that fits instead. Think of trees planted under telephone lines and/or utility wires. Topping the trees is expensive, destroys habitat, and is a bit unsightly. Trees are often topped (coppiced) to protect a view as well. Some forethought may be the best strategy.

And, often we prune for therapy. Deadheading is a term applied to the pruning of spent blossoms (i.e., those that have been pollinated and have subsequently dropped their petals). Removing spent blossoms aids continued flowering. The time spent with this activity in the garden can be quite pleasing and therapeutic.

© Sadovnikova Olga/
Shutterstock.com

Pruning Targets

The first order of business in any prune activity is the removal of dead, dying, and diseased plant parts. One might hope that this is obvious, but unfortunately it is not. As mentioned earlier, insects and their larvae thrive in decaying matter. Dead wood and dying parts of the plant provide prime habitat, and must be excised.

Remove competing leaders. When two leading branches grow equally dominate toward the top of the tree, a narrow crotch is formed where they originate. When the branches grow in diameter, much pressure and stress is placed at the intersection of the two branches (the crotch). Heavy winds, rain, or snow can cause a split, break, and extensive tearing. Removing one allows the other branch to grow as intended.

Crowded branches are much like competing leaders, because the junction where the two branches meet at the edge of the trunk is too narrow. When the branches grow in diameter, excess pressure is applied to the base of each branch. Deformation and splitting will occur.

PRUNING

Lecture Contents (*continued*)

Pruning Targets (*continued*)

Cutting branches indiscriminately can lead to serious disruptions in the processes of respiration and photosynthesis. The tree's leaves and canopy are there for a reason. The process of removing all but stubs is a popular, but detrimental practice. The tree, in stress, produces suckers (originating from the soil) and water sprouts (originating from positions on the plant above ground). These are easily recognized by their near straight vertical growth with increased space between each node (indicating rapid growth). Suckers and water sprouts grow vigorously when the tree is poorly pruned. They are weakly connected and must be removed when they grow beyond a 2-in. diameter themselves.

The "*one-third*" rule is a practice wherein a branch is left attached that is at least one-third the diameter of the branch from which it originates. Where branch "B" is a branch that arises out of a leading branch "A," then "B" must be equal to or greater than one-third "A." This assures that transpiration will continue, without malformed and weakly attached suckers and sprouts.

PRUNING OF ROSE BUSH

© Svetlana Zhukova/
Shutterstock.com

When and How to Prune

Most spring-flowering shrubs bloom on wood that grew the previous year. The previous year's growth is termed "old wood." If you prune a plant in the fall, and it is one that flowers on old wood, you are pruning *off* the next season's buds. If you prune a plant in the spring that blooms on "new wood," then you are also cutting off the current season's flowering.

Pruning ought not to be performed during drought, when plants are stressed (although many plants don't often "experience" drought stress due to extensive irrigation). Pruning also not be practiced during threat of freeze and subfreezing weather. Pruning when the tree is young (when the branches are smaller) allows for smaller wounds. A plant's ability to heal from prunes (wounds) depends on size and number of wounds. It also depends on age, vigor, and health of tree, and species. Hardwood, slow-growing, long-lived trees seal faster than fast-growing, softwood species of short life span.

Pruning techniques vary, depending on intended result, and depending on species of plant. We talk of shaping a shrub or tree and consider "heading back" or "shearing." We rejuvenate a plant with renewal and rejuvenation prune techniques.

PRUNING

Lecture Contents (*continued*)

When and How to Prune (*continued*)

Heading back is used to control the size of the shrub. In a heading back technique, a branch is removed at the junction of another lateral branch. Heading back is best done when new growth is complete.

Neglected shrubs (depending on species) can be restored to vigor by a "hard pruning," wherein all stems are pruned to ground level. Hard pruning (aka rejuvenation pruning) is best done when the plant is in dormancy (winter through early spring).

A renewal prune is the removal of old, overgrown stems or canes. This is usually done over a period of 3 to 4 years, and one-third of the stems are removed each time (this assures that ample leaves and stems remain to foster adequate photosynthesis). This practice too is best during the dormant season.

Shearing is a technique for creating a formal hedge or parterre. The top of the hedge must not shade the bottom half of the hedge. Sunlight must reach the lower branches. Therefore, the top of the planned hedge must be narrower than the bottom portion.

Hand-operated cutting tools include hand pruners, loppers, saws, and shears. Hand pruners are used for branches ½-in. diameter or less. Loppers are long-handled pruners, and apply in the removal of branches to 2-in. thick. Hand pruners and loppers are available as two types: anvil pruner/lopper or bypass pruner/lopper. An anvil pruner or lopper is for removing dead wood. A bypass pruner (or lopper) is used to remove green/live wood. Branches greater than 2-in. diameter are recommended to be removed by saw. Tools ought to be sharp and clean, to prevent the spread of disease.

The union where a branch is attached to the main stem or trunk is termed the branch collar. The cells that seal a wound are housed in the branch collar; the collar must remain intact. A torn branch collar presents a wound that will not adequately seal, and thus will not subsequently heal. To protect the branch collar from tearing when a limb greater than 2-in. diameter is removed, a relief cut is first required.

A relief cut of approximately one-fifth the branch diameter is made on the underside of the branch to be removed. A second cut is made to excise the limb. A third and final cut is made through the subject limb, adjacent to, but not disturbing, the intact branch collar.

Lecture Contents (*continued*)

When and How to Prune (*continued*)

The first portable chainsaw was developed and patented in 1918 by Canadian millwright James Shand. Chainsaws and power shears are, of course, used extensively in the tree and shrub pruning industry. A note on two-stroke engines is therefore in order. Two-stroke engines are light in weight and high in power.

They are also, unfortunately, light in pollution controls, and high in harmful exhaust. Simply stated, two-stroke engines (as opposed to the more efficient four-stroke version) emit unconsumed or inefficiently burned fuel (the most poisonous kind) in their exhaust. Using a two-stroke engine for 1 hour is the equivalent of driving a new car from Los Angeles to New York. Ask the question whether pruning is necessary then, before embarking on a project, especially if two-stroke engines are needed.

© MarBom/Shutterstock. com

Purpose of Pruning

1. Size control—To keep plants from overgrowing
2. Health improvement—To remove dead branches and diseased limbs/to encourage stronger branch structure
3. Appearance improvement—To remove scraggly branches, dead flowers

Basic Tree Pruning

1. Removal of double leaders
   - To maintain a central leader, avoiding the cause of a failure

2. Removal of excess scaffold branches
   - To be cut beyond the bark ridge or collar (shoulder ring)
   - To avoid *topping*—To remove the central leader and to cut the side branches rapidly
   - To avoid *lion tailing*—To cut the leaves and smaller branches in the center leaving the inner parts stripped
   - *Limbing up*—To remove lower branches positioned too low on the trunk
   - *Desuckering*—Removal of shoots at the base or lower trunk (*water sprouts*)

- *CODIT* (**CO**mpartmentalization of **D**ecay **I**n **T**rees)—Plant's behavior of compartmentalizing the infection and growing new tissues to counteract the detrimental effects of decay microorganism

Lecture Contents (*continued*)

When and How to Prune (*continued*)

3. Drop crotch pruning
    - To reduce tree crowns, lowering the crown height, for example, under the power lines
    - To cut back the tallest terminal (vertical) branch to a large lateral (horizontal) branch—Diameter of the lateral branch to which the terminal branch is cut MUST be at least one-third the diameter of the terminal branch being cut

4. Pollarding
    - For deciduous tree pruning
    - To create a denser head of foliage
    - To develop swollen limb ends of multiple branch collars

Basic Shrub Pruning

1. Thinning
    - To remove the oldest stems at ground level to encourage refoliation of the bottom

2. Heading back
    - To remove straggly growth of to limit size
    - To cut twigs or small branches back to the point where the cut is hidden by the remaining foliage

3. Renewal pruning
    - To rejuvenate and shorten overgrown shrubs
    - In early spring before new growth starts
    - To cut back all the branches to stubs 2- to 3-in. long

Special Shrub Pruning

1. Espalier
    - Stylized training of shrub against a wall or trellis
    - To start when a plant is small

2. Topiary
    - Shaping shrubs or small trees into certain shapes
    - To start when a plant is young

PRUNING

Lecture Contents (*continued*)

When and How to Prune (*continued*)

Hedge Pruning

- Thinning and heading back once or twice a year
- Formal hedges to shear every 2 weeks during the growing season
- Selecting the correct hedge shape: Very important for maintaining hedge health

Groundcover Pruning

- Most of groundcover not necessary to require regular pruning
- To remove older bed of groundcover with leafless stems

Timing of Pruning

- Timing of pruning not affecting the health of plants
- Early spring as a traditional pruning time
  - Easier to determine which parts to be removed
  - To control new growing direction

- Light pruning two to three times annually

Basic Pruning Cuts

Pinching
- To pinch off a terminal bud with your thumb and forefinger without cutting
- To stop the stem from elongating and encourages bushy growth
- For annual and perennial flowers and on some vegetables; effective for directing growth on small-leafed shrubs to give the plant an even shape

Heading
- To cut farther back on the shoot than pinching
- To make the cut right above the leaf, encouraging dense growth
- More aggressive approach than pinching when shaping certain small shrubs and flowering perennials

PRUNING

Lecture Contents (*continued*)

When and How to Prune (*continued*)

Thinning
- To reduce the bulk of a plant with minimal regrowth
- To remove an entire stem or branch, either back to its point of origin on the main stem or to the point where it joins another branch

Shearing
- To create a hedge or a bush with spherical or square form
- To stimulate many buds to produce new growth
- To cut right through leaves
- For small-leafed plants

PRUNING

Relevant Links

TEDTalk

How to Grow a Forest in
Your Backyard

https://www.ted.com/talks/shubhendu_sharma_how_to_grow_a_
forest_in_your_backyard?utm_campaign=tedspread&utm_
medium=referral&utm_source=tedcomshare

An Engineer's Vision for
Tiny Forests, Everywhere

https://www.ted.com/talks/shubhendu_sharma_an_engineers_
vision_for_tiny_forests_everywhere?utm_campaign=tedspread&utm_
medium=referral&utm_source=tedcomshare

Wiki (Reference purpose only)

Pruning   https://en.wikipedia.org/wiki/Pruning
Pollarding   https://en.wikipedia.org/wiki/Pollarding
Professional Landcare   https://en.wikipedia.org/wiki/National_Association_of_Landscape_
Network (PLANET)   Professionals

Others

Tree Pruning Guide   https://www.arborday.org/trees/pruning/index.cfm?Trackin-
gID=1817&utm_source=Tree%2BBook&utm_medium=Cata-
log&utm_campaign=The%2BTree%2BBook&utm_term=pruning

Tree Care Tips & Techniques   https://www.arborday.org/trees/tips/when-to-prune.cfm
Pruning Small Trees and Shrubs   http://ceventura.ucanr.edu/Environmental_Horticulture/Landscape/
Pruning/

Urban Forest Program Manual   http://file.lacounty.gov/SDSInter/dpr/184720_UFPMANUAL080211.
pdf

How to Prune Trees   https://www.fs.usda.gov/Internet/FSE_DOCUMENTS/fsbdev7_016046.
pdf

Quizzes

© Davidovka/Shutterstock.
com

1. Describe three primary purposes of pruning.

2. What does CODIT stand for? And, describe it briefly.

3. Describe three types of basic shrub cutting methods.

TRENDS IN SUSTAINABLE HORTICULTURE—URBAN FARMING

Relevant Words

Brown field, Carbon footprint, Community-supported agriculture (CSA), Deforestation, Food safety, Land acquisition, Permaculture, Rain forest, Sustainability, Urban farming

Lab Objective

To observe the practice of sustainable horticulture and to identify the benefit from it, comparing it to traditional horticulture

Lab Assignment

- Conduct an interview with a person who is in new trends of sustainable horticulture, such as urban farming.
- Identify pros and cons, if any, in focusing on sustainable horticulture business.
- Assess the future trends based upon the interview.

Lecture Outlines

❖ Professions in Sustainable Horticulture
❖ Trends in Urban Farming
❖ Understanding the Current Job Opportunities
❖ Future Trends in Sustainable Horticulture

© Lorelyn Medina/
Shutterstock.com

TRENDS IN SUSTAINABLE HORTICULTURE—URBAN FARMING

Lecture Contents

© Mario Breda/
Shutterstock.com

Sustainable Horticulture

The Amazon rain forest is the world's largest rain forest. It covers over 2.1 million sq. miles (5.5 million sq. km). There are over 390 billion trees. It is dense, wild, and diverse. Together, its trees absorb two billion metric tons of carbon annually, and produce 20% of the oxygen we breathe. Indeed, the Amazon rain forest functions as the "lungs of our planet." It is a hugely significant (yet largely invisible) contribution to the entire globe.

But efforts to protect this rain forest, and others like it, are challenged by large-scale corporate farming practices and profit potential. Land is cleared to grow soybeans, fruits, vegetables, and cheap cotton. Deforestation in the Amazon has been as high as 9,000 sq. miles a day. We must be wiser with regard to how we use our lands to grow our foods. Human health and food security for a growing global population depend on it.

Fortunately, growing public consciousness has elevated demand for food grown without poisons and/or environmental degradation. Calls for sustainable practices have gained traction on a global basis. Sustainable, fair, and socially responsible practices for growing and supplying food are no longer mere options.

There is increased demand for careers in horticulture that are based on principles of sustainability and ecology. According to a recent analysis of job opportunities in agriculture, there are 57,900 job openings in agriculture and related fields each year. But just 35,400 students graduate annually with a bachelor's degree or higher in agriculture. Opportunity is strong (https://stockbridge.cns.umass.edu/SFF-good-work).

Horticulturalists with skills in sustainability have a competitive advantage in the horticulture job market. Employers need professionals who can develop, implement, and manage sustainable practices in urban farming, wholesale grower facilities, food production, nurseries stock production, fruit and nut growers, vineyards, and botanic gardens. There is a need for qualified professionals with the skills to take on the challenges of the sustainable revolution.

Some of the careers offered in sustainable horticulture include research associates, cultivation technicians, greenhouse technicians, growers, propagators, and many more. A sampling of job openings brings forth the following job description summaries:

Sustainable Native Garden Supervisor: Proficient in the pruning needs of various native plants with the ability to teach others.

Lecture Contents (*continued*)

Sustainable Horticulture (*continued*)

Cultivation Production Analyst: Responsible for managing propagation, cultivation, and harvest data for internal production and cost analyses, as well as managing state compliance track and trace software.

Sustainable Agriculture Coordinator: Establish, develop, and strengthen connections/partnerships with other local nonprofits, businesses, schools, faith/interfaith organizations, and other groups.

Sustainable Agriculture Specialist: Provide farmers and ranchers with information and technical assistance on environmentally sound practices for agronomic and horticultural crops and livestock.

Career potential is also found among the urban farming movement. There are tens of thousands of acres of land capable of producing crops and that are suitable for farming in and around urban centers, and it is indeed possible to create an abundance of healthy food there.

Community-supported agriculture (CSA) is another promising opportunity in sustainable horticulture. CSA is a system whereby local farm good consumers subscribe to the harvest of a local farmer. The harvest is distributed either weekly or biweekly as a box of produce or other farm goods. Some CSAs provide for contributions of labor in lieu of a portion of subscription costs.

Establishing an urban farm is not an easy task. As with starting any business, there are numerous considerations and challenges to research and strategies to implement. Funding, adequate space, and water source are of paramount concern. Land acquisition is expensive. Real estate prices do not necessarily favor "a good cause." If the land is not owned by the farm, of course, perpetuity is uncertain.

City or county land that is set aside for parks and recreation ought to be considered for possible collaboration. The Orange County Great Park is one such example. Voters approved the 688 acre park "conversion" in 2001 (the land was part of the former Marine Corp Air Station El Toro). The park has traditional amenities such as soccer fields, volley ball courts, tennis courts, and an arts complex. Proponents were also able to include the establishment of the Farm and Food Lab.

Lecture Contents (*continued*)

Sustainable Horticulture (*continued*)

The Farm and Food Lab is "a working and dynamic organic horticulture area with a mission to educate visitors about gardening, inspire innovative and unique ideas, and facilitate a thriving community of people working in partnership." It is an interactive outdoor classroom, featuring raised-bed gardens, fruit trees, and vertical gardening (http://www.cityofirvine.org/orange-county-great-park/farm-food-lab).

The Beacon Food Forest Permaculture Project in Seattle, Washington, is 5 acres garden 2.5 miles out of downtown Seattle. It was designed as an edible forest for the local community, which also "rehabilitates the local ecosystem." From their website: "Join us to improve public health by regenerating our public land into an edible forest ecosystem. We work to reduce agricultural climate impact, improve our local food security, provide educational opportunities, and celebrate growing food for the benefit of all species" (https://beaconfoodforest.org/). Movements such as this are setting current trends.

Another option may be to lease land from the local power company. Land beneath power wires along the tower corridor is available for various uses. Southern California Edison, which supplies power to 19 million residents of southern California, has 50,000 sq. miles of land within such a corridor. Nurseries and tree farms have been leasing in this manner since the 1960s.

Brownfield sites are sites that have been developed prior, but are not in use at present. There is movement and progress to convert former factory sites to community amenities. Urban farms are possible. If land is acquired that needs rehabilitation, it is important to test the soil for contaminants.

Zoning constraints may present an obstacle. A discussion of agriculture in commercial or residential zones is often opposed. Research whether an urban farm is allowed, and whether chickens, bees, and/or small animals can be included.

The potential water source for the farm must be considered. Is there a public supply? Crops need water. Farmers and guests need water. And vegetables need to be washed. Consider using gray water for irrigation of fruit and nut trees. An assessment of drainage is needed. Visit the proposed site during rainfall to see whether water puddles or drains well. Both too little water and too much water must be addressed.

TRENDS IN SUSTAINABLE HORTICULTURE—URBAN FARMING

Lecture Contents (*continued*)

Sustainable Horticulture (*continued*)

Funding and budgeting are an integral part of an urban farm business plan. "It is important for farmers to grow and/or create products that can easily be marketed or are in demand. To do this, talk to restaurants, grocery stores, farmers' market managers, local food producers, and community members to find out where there are gaps or marketing opportunities." Learn about the processes and costs. Create a business plan that includes marketing strategies and a budget (https://ucanr.edu/sites/UrbanAg/Starting_an_Urban_Farm/).

Food safety and food quality concerns must be planned for and strictly adhered to. Many fruits and vegetables require refrigeration upon harvest. Apples, beans, carrots, corn, and many others fall into this category. They must be kept fresh for marketability.

Pest and disease management is also of paramount concern. Most urban farms employ the less toxic methods of integrated pest management (IPM). These principles help with food, employee, and public safety as well, as synthetic insecticides and herbicides are avoided.

The largest urban farm in America was established in South Central Los Angeles in 1994. It was a 14-acre oasis called the South Central Farm. It was created on vacant land owned by the city of Los Angeles for low-income families to farm on. The farm thrived for 10 years, but was then sold in 2004. Battle lines were drawn between the farmers, who disputed the validity of the sale, and a developer.

The demise of the South Central Farm was featured in a Scott Hamilton film titled *The Garden*, which earned a 2009 Academy Award nomination for Best Documentary Feature. The film highlighted challenging questions of equality and justice for the impoverished families.

Activists helped raise millions of dollars for the farmers to acquire the land from the developer. But the farmers were evicted anyway. The site was bulldozed on July 5, 2006, among strong protest and acts of civil disobedience. The developer stood firm in his statement that he just "didn't like" the farmers. At this date, the land remains a vacant lot. Some experts say that issues of social justice must be considered.

Growing food closer to where people live eliminates a huge "carbon footprint" associated with shipping and transit exposures. Plastic packaging is reduced. Pollution is reduced.

TRENDS IN SUSTAINABLE HORTICULTURE—URBAN FARMING

Lecture Contents (*continued*)

Sustainable Horticulture (*continued*)

Fuel is conserved, and less rubber tires are consumed in the process. Most would argue correctly as well, that the vegetables are even just simply fresher.

Urban farms offer many other benefits as well. Youth, adults, and seniors connect with the source of their food. They learn of healthy soil and planet Earth. They connect with nature. Increased awareness of health and wellness ensues.

Urban farms and CSAs need to be a part of the urban planning process. They are certainly as important as community parks and recreation facilities. A paradigm shift is in order. Urban farms can uplift a community, and ought to be considered an asset.

TRENDS IN SUSTAINABLE HORTICULTURE—URBAN FARMING

Lecture Contents (*continued*)

Sustainable Horticulture (*continued*)

© Falara/Shutterstock.com

© cube29/Shutterstock.com

TRENDS IN SUSTAINABLE HORTICULTURE—URBAN FARMING

Relevant Links

TEDTalk
How Urban Agriculture
    Is Transforming Detroit

https://www.ted.com/talks/devita_davison_how_urban_agriculture_is_transforming_detroit?utm_campaign=tedspread&utm_medium=referral&utm_source=tedcomshare

Why I Create Pop-Up
    Farms in My City

https://youtu.be/r-fHY43qLWs

Wiki (Reference purpose only)
Urban Agriculture
Permaculture
American Society for
    Horticulture Science

https://en.wikipedia.org/wiki/Urban_agriculture
https://en.wikipedia.org/wiki/Permaculture
https://www.ashs.org/page/CareerPaths

Others
TheLandlovers.org
AgCareers.com
HorticulturalJobs.com
Plant Science and
    Horticulture
Horticulture: Career to be
    Proud of
I Love My Job in
    Horticulture
From Couture to Compost:
    Blossoming Career in
    Horticulture

http://www.thelandlovers.org/careers.asp
https://www.agcareers.com
https://www.horticulturaljobs.com
https://youtu.be/j-zJqgOjiCM

https://youtu.be/MJwcZglGZbQ

https://youtu.be/52Fp1PN740k

https://www.theguardian.com/careers/couture-to-compost-blossoming-career-horticulture

TRENDS IN SUSTAINABLE HORTICULTURE—URBAN FARMING

Quizzes

© Davidovka/Shutterstock. com

1. What was the largest urban farm in America established in 1994? And, what was the primary reason to be closed in 2004?

2. What does CSA stand for? And, describe it briefly.

3. List three examples of careers offered in sustainable horticulture.

SUSTAINABLE LANDSCAPE DESIGN—WELLNESS GARDEN

Relevant Words

Allelochemical, Antimicrobial, Aroma therapy, Contemplative garden, Cycle of Creation, Cycle of Destruction, *Feng shui*, *Genius Loci* (Sense of Place), *Mycobacterium vaccae*, Nature fascination, Neurotransmitter, Park prescription, Phytoncides, Serotonin, *Shinrin-yoku*, Wellness garden

Lab Objective

To observe and research the difference between sustainable landscape designs and traditional ones, and to describe the relationship between people and their surrounding environment.

Lab Assignment

- Explore your neighborhood.
- Identify any gardens or parks that may serve as "contemplating" places.
- Observe people using the space and record how the space has been utilized for "therapeutic" functions.
- Describe the positive impacts wellness gardens have on our daily lives.

Lecture Outlines

© dizain/Shutterstock.com

❖ Role of Garden for Wellness
❖ Benefit of Wellness Garden
❖ Sustainable Landscape Design as a Tool for Creating a *"Well-Being"* Living Environment

| CHAPTER 17 | # SUSTAINABLE LANDSCAPE DESIGN—WELLNESS GARDEN |

Lecture Contents

© Giuseppe_R/Shutterstock.
com

Sustainable Landscape

A garden is a planned space, usually outdoors, set aside for the display, cultivation, preservation, study, or enjoyment of plants and other forms of nature. To many, a garden is also a place of contemplation; thought, reflection, meditation, consideration, reverie, and introspection. A garden designed for contemplation can aid the rejuvenation of a person's body, mind, and spirit.

The design of gardens and landscapes that promotes wellness and human well-being originated more than 3,500 years ago. *Feng shui* was, and is still used, to situate the human environment in a place of optimal energy. The practice is based on the idea that the landscape spaces around us influence the people who use the space.

Wellness gardens play a role in the health of all individuals: the sick and infirmed, the strong and able, and users of all ages. A garden can be a restorative and healthy place in many ways. Outdoor physical activity is shown to have positive impacts on a person's health. A stroll through a garden and a restful period of contemplation in one are both equally restorative and therapeutic.

The University of California, Davis, has a "wellness garden" at the Student Health and Wellness Center central to the campus. They strive to lead by example, that today's universities will fulfill their duty to "provide nurturing environments that cultivate the 'whole student.'" The wellness garden fosters "critical thinking and workforce competitiveness," but also holistic well-being. "Wellness encompasses a healthy body, a sound mind and a tranquil spirit" (https://shcs.ucdavis.edu/about/student-wellness-garden). The UC Davis Wellness Garden plays a role "by serving as a catalyst for renewal" for human well-being.

The Los Angeles County Arboretum and Botanic Garden has a program of Yoga in the garden. Their gentle all-levels garden Yoga accesses the Arboretum's natural tranquility to "deepen your body's capacity to heal and strengthen itself" (https://www.arboretum.org/learn/classes-year-around/fitness-classes/?gclid=EAIaIQobChMIjYTj1f6G3gIV-1I2zCh0iEQSwEAMYAiAAEgI8sfD_BwE).

East Boston residents and the East Boston Neighborhood Health Center (EBNHC) created their wellness garden in a former parking lot with 30 raised beds in an "initiative to support healthier lifestyles." Participants of the wellness garden are all patients at EBNHC. (https://www.ebnhc.org/en/food-access/wellness-garden.html)

SUSTAINABLE LANDSCAPE DESIGN—WELLNESS GARDEN

Lecture Contents (*continued*)

Sustainable Landscape (*continued*)

There is growing evidence that participants in gardening activities report positive mood shifts. "Nature fascination," sensory joy, peacefulness, and tranquility are often cited. Research indicates that marked psychological benefits arise from being in a natural environment. One study asked people what kind of place they went to when feeling troubled, upset, or in grief. Natural settings were predominantly cited (https://www.healthdesign.org/sites/default/files/Gardens%20in%20HC%20Facility%20Visits.pdf).

Shinrin-yoku is a term that means "taking in the forest atmosphere" or "forest bathing." Japanese forest bathing is based on the belief that our connection with nature leads to abundance and good health. It is based on the notion that a connection with nature is of significant health benefit. Several theories have been proposed as to why.

Phytoncides are antimicrobial allelochemical volatile organic compounds derived from plants (they are what we smell when we walk in the forest). Some suggest that phytoncides have a physiological effect on our stress levels. Others suggest that bird song, trickling water, and the sound of rustling leaves are physiologically calming as well.

Further, scientists are compiling evidence that the soil bacterium *Mycobacterium vaccae* acts to stimulate the production of serotonin. Serotonin is a neurotransmitter involved in the regulation of a person's sleep, appetite, and aggression. Serotonin is also a key player in mood, anxiety, fear, and general sense of well-being. Researchers immunized lab mice with the bacterium and found it to promote stress resiliency.

Thus, current thought suggests that being with the soil, working with it, and playing in it are good for you. The data support a strategy of "reintroducing" humans to microorganisms in soil and nature to "promote optimal health and wellness" (http://www.pnas.org/content/pnas/113/22/E3130.full.pdf).

Health professionals and practitioners of well-being seem to be getting on board. A *New York Times* article by Amitha Kalaichandran, MD (July 12, 2018) is titled "Take a Walk in the Woods. Doctor's Orders." *Dr. Kalaichandran* cites several examples.

At the University of California, San Francisco, Benioff Children's Hospital in Oakland, *Dr. Nooshin Razani*, a pediatric infectious disease doctor and director of the Center for Nature and Health, administers the "Shine" program, in coordination with the Regional Parks District. The program offers "park prescriptions." The program aims to improve accessibility to nature for low-income children.

Lecture Contents (*continued*)

Sustainable Landscape (*continued*)

Northside Hospital Cancer Institute in Atlanta offers forest therapy as part of a pilot project in collaboration with the Chattahoochee Nature Center. Patients are taken out for 4-hour nature sessions, as a critical part of their well-being.

And, *Dr. Suzanne Bartlett Hackenmiller*, an obstetrician-gynecologist based in Cedar Falls, Iowa, is certified through the Association of Nature and Forest Therapy. She guides her patients through nature and through an experience of the different senses. Patients practice listening to nearby sounds and observing how far they may extend or smelling the air. It is like guided meditation (https://www.nytimes.com/2018/07/12/well/take-a-walk-in-the-woods-doctors-orders.html).

Several factors must be considered to achieve a living environment that fosters well-being. To design a garden that's in harmony with its surroundings, start by considering, *and appreciating*, existing natural features of the site. Contours and resulting drainage, direction of the sun, wind flow, views, rock outcroppings (if any), and existing plant materials must be analyzed. The use of existing (and local) materials not only contributes to goals of sustainability but helps provide the "*Genius Loci*" (Sense of Place) as discussed in Chapter 11.

Consider, as would a practitioner of *feng shui*, the "five elements" needed in a well-balanced garden, and examine the presence or absence of same. The five elements, as suggested in the practice are fire, earth, metal, water, and wood.

The *fire* element is expressed by fire itself, of course, color representing fire, or spikey and triangular shapes. For example, candles and fireplaces can naturally represent the fire elements.

The *earth* element is represented with earthen materials, colors, and/or square shapes and rectangles. The presence of this element helps assure "grounding."

Precious *metals* are associated with refinement and grace. From ancient to modern cultures, metals have represented wealth and status. Most metal is thought of as resistant and intense. The metal element is achieved with metal itself, and with round and half-round features or plants. Metal can also be associated with the colors white or gray.

In nature, *water* wends its way around obstacles to ultimately find its destination. The water element represents the ability to yield without compromising a goal. Water features,

Lecture Contents (*continued*)

Sustainable Landscape (*continued*)

meandering shapes, and the color of water in plant selection or hardscape add to this element and enhance its effect.

The *wood* element (represented by wood, the colors of wood, or columnar objects) represents upward growth, and, as such, is needed in a rejuvenating and wellness garden setting.

Inclusion of these elements alone, however, does not lead to success in the creation of a balanced design for well-being. Actual informed placement and relation of the elements to one another are of significant concern to the practitioner of *feng shui*.

In what is known as the Cycle of Destruction, placement of the water element adjacent to a fire element creates a clash, as water douses fire. And fire melts metal (thus, fire and metal elements need be separated). Metal cuts wood (another destructive cycle arrangement or placement). And wood draws elements (takes) from the earth.

The Cycle of Creation, on the other hand (i.e., "good" *feng shui*) has the fire element aligned with the earth element (fire "produces" earth). The earth element is aligned with the metal element (elements in earth form metal). Water is positioned with wood (water helps wood grow). And finally, wood is positioned with consideration of fire (wood feeds fire).

A contemplative garden must engage the senses. As written by *St. Bernard* (1090–1153) of a patient at his hospice in Clairvaux, France, "The lovely green of herb and tree nourishes his eyes. . . . . The choir of painted birds caresses his ears . . . the earth breathes with fruitfulness, and the (patient) himself with eyes, ears, and nostrils, drinks in the delights of colors, songs, and perfumes" (https://www.healthdesign.org/sites/default/files/Gardens%20in%20HC%20Facility%20Visits.pdf).

St. Bernard's account of the sensory delights has some interesting parallels with the benefits of gardens today. Sights, sounds, and smells still play a critical role.

Humans have used aromatherapy for thousands of years. It is the art and science of using plant extracts for health and well-being. Aromatherapy enhances both physical and emotional health. But aromatic oils need not be extracted to be effective. Plants produce green leaf volatiles in their living state. The strong odor emitted by many plants is affected by a variety of factors, such as temperature and sunlight. There are many diverse trees, shrubs, flowers, and herbs to choose from.

Lecture Contents (*continued*)

Sustainable Landscape (*continued*)

Selecting plants that attract birds will add auditory pleasure. Willows (*Salix spp.*) signify water. Willows thus invite birds. Certain plants, such as *Populus tremuloides* (Quaking aspen), contribute sound when their leaves flutter in the breeze (the leaf petiole is flat, which causes the leaves to "flap" instead of twirl).

Shade and seating (out of the wind) are also critical considerations. One must remain comfortable in a contemplative and healing garden. Shade is cooling and soothing. Seating allows for rest, rejuvenation, and community.

Wellness gardens must be safe and secure. Well-defined perimeters enhance focus and provide opportunities for privacy to the greatest extent possible, especially in a residential setting.

Discussion herein has presented the theory that nature is good for us. Designed with sustainability in mind, wellness gardens are intensive outdoor environments for restoration, therapy, and for social exchanges.

© Lorelyn Medina/
Shutterstock.com

Horticulture Therapy

As the Global Strategy for the Prevention and Control of Non-Communicable Diseases (NCD) indicates, NCD can best be addressed by a combination of primary prevention interventions targeting whole populations, by measures that target high-risk individuals and by improved access to essential healthcare interventions for people with NCDs.

—WHO, 2006

Definition

1. Healing and sensory gardens
   - Passive health benefits
   - Healing by building sustainable communities
   - Improving the mood of the people with local aesthetics and biodiversity
   - Place to meditate, to sit, to chat, to relax, and to get away
   - Vital in preventing illness through sensing nature ("harm from a deficiency of outdoor experience")
   - Pleasing in visual, audible, tactile, scented, and tasty experience

SUSTAINABLE LANDSCAPE DESIGN—WELLNESS GARDEN

Lecture Contents (*continued*)

Horticulture Therapy (*continued*)

2. Therapeutic gardens
   - In corrective and healthcare environment
   - Horticultural therapy garden (social and therapeutic horticulture)
   - Active healing through gardening
   - Raised garden design—Inclusive, accessible
   - More structured program

History

Gardens as paradise
- Garden of Eden
- Islamic garden—"River of Life"
- Monastery garden—Physics garden (medical), kitchen garden (food), orchard
- Asian Zen Garden—Aesthetically pleasing, meditation

Gardens for Health and Well-Being: Lifestyle and Diseases

1. Healthy, active lifestyle as the prevention of disease
2. Social and environmental determinants of disease
3. Noncommunicable disease (NCD)—Preventable (provision of healing green space)
4. *Green prescription*—Community walking, exercise, nutrition on prescription (most cost effective)
5. Healing landscape intervention—Longevity, quality of life, and general well-being of communities
6. Urban space degradation—Appreciation for urban space determined by the quality of green space
7. Quality of landscape = Quality of life
   - Increase of biodiversity
   - Habitat restoration
   - Heat island effect reduction
   - Storm water runoff reduction
   - Positive interaction between human and nature
   - Interaction improvement

Lecture Contents (*continued*)

Horticulture Therapy (*continued*)

Low-Impact Urban Design and Development (LIUDD)

1. Sustainable communities = Healthy communities
2. To promote urban sustainability and health through effective management of storm water, waste, energy, transport, and ecosystem
3. Community activities

Healing Garden for Post Traumatic Stress Disorder (PTSD)

1. Natural leafy shade
2. Clear sight lines to give a sense of safety and security
3. Homelike environment—No institutional furniture
4. Flat walking surfaces without camber
5. Reduced glare
6. Lush planting to absorb sound and create a feeling of oasis
7. Positive sound interference
8. Wildlife-attracting plants
9. Abundant seating
10. Areas for covered, playful, contemplation
11. Opportunities for light and exercise

Shinrin-yoku (*Forest Bathing*)

1. Forest walking and health—Promoted by Forest Agency of Japan
2. Green exercise—Physical movement in a natural setting
3. Increased activity of natural killer (NK) cells—To boost stress resistance
4. Presence of phytoncides (wood essential oils), antimicrobial volatile organic compounds emitted from trees—highly concentrated in forest air, none in the city air
5. Active interaction with nature, gardening, or yard work—*Mycobacterium vaccae* (bacterium found in soil, triggering the release of serotonin, a hormone to decrease anxiety and depression)

Lecture Contents (*continued*)

Horticulture Therapy (*continued*)

Stress Reduction Theory

1. Sense of control (actual and perceived) and access to privacy
2. Social support
3. Physical movement and exercise
4. Positive natural distraction through contact with nature

Therapeutic Garden Design Guidelines

1. Safety, security, and privacy
2. Accessibility: Americans with Disabilities Act (ADA), universal design
3. Physical and emotional comfort
4. Positive distraction: getting away
5. Engagement with nature (biophilia)
6. Proper maintenance and aesthetics with sustainability

Therapeutic Garden Criteria

1. Raised planting bed and containers with various sizes and heights
2. Vertical garden promoting sitting and standing work
3. Ground-level planting, avoiding toxic plants
4. Collection of well-maintained plants
5. Lockable storage and seating areas, water features
6. Protection from sun, rain, and wind
7. Restrooms and drinking fountain
8. Garden views
9. Safety and security
10. inclusive

SUSTAINABLE LANDSCAPE DESIGN—WELLNESS GARDEN

Lecture Contents (*continued*)

© world of vector/ Shutterstock.com

Feng 風 (Wind) Shui 水 (Water)

1. An ancient Chinese discipline or art form of placement traceable to prehistoric eras:
   - The practice of feng shui was established over 6,000 years ago
   - Subjects of nature, such as physics, philosophy, astronomy, and astrology

2. The simple interaction of humans and their environments
3. Life improvements by positioning or designing the surroundings in harmony with principles of natural energy flow
4. Art of placement to bring balance, comfort, and harmony.
5. Direct carriers of chi (life force)

The Basic Principles

- The concept of Yin and Yang along with five elements
- Harmony in immediate surroundings through careful arrangement of objects and colors

Yin and Yang

- Concept of duality, such as light and dark, smooth and rough, hot and cold, and male and female
- "The principle of Yin and Yang is the foundation of the entire universe, and, it underlies everything in creation. Too much of any one thing may cause disharmony."

Chi 氣 (Energy)

The governing life source of all living matter, divided into two opposite forces:

Yin (female) and *Yang* (male)—To be balanced

Five Elements

Earth	Light yellow, sandy, earthy, light brown/Square/ Rocks, ceramics
Fire	Red, dark yellow, orange, purple, pink/triangular/candles, fireplaces
Metal	White, gray/Round/Electronic devices, silver frames
Water	Blue, black/Wavy/Fountain, aquarium
Wood	green, brown / Rectangular / Living plants

Lecture Contents (*continued*)

Feng 風 (Wind) Shui 水 (Water) (*continued*)

Bagua-dou 八卦圖 (Eight-Section Map)

A basic tool to learn which parts of a space, such as a home, office, room, or yard, correlate with particular areas of life. Once identified which area of a space corresponds to which life aspiration, then surrounding environment can be enhanced to achieve the goals.

Mitigating Method Examples

- Unblock pathways—Unobstructed traffic pattern
- Add plants or vegetation—Symbol of life and growth
- Add pink hue—Warm color to enhance *chi*
- De-clutter—Feeling of calm and relaxation
- Mirror—To reflect positive energy
- Avoid sharp lines—Sharp corners emitting negative energy
- Round is GOOD

Color Theory

- Green—Symbolizing nature/representative of life and hope
- Yellow—Power
- Red/purple—Lucky

SUSTAINABLE LANDSCAPE DESIGN—WELLNESS GARDEN

Lecture Contents (*continued*)

Feng 風 (Wind) Shui 水 (Water) (*continued*)

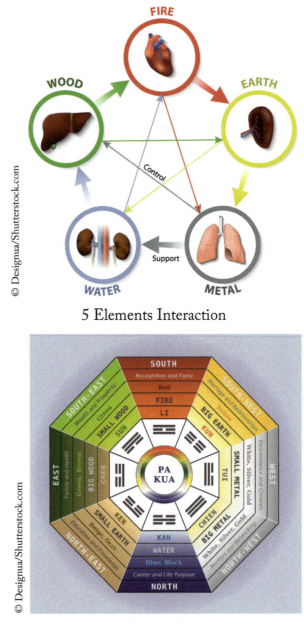

5 Elements Interaction

Bagua-dou

SUSTAINABLE LANDSCAPE DESIGN—WELLNESS GARDEN

Relevant Links

TEDTalk

How Can Countries Measure the Well-Being of Their Citizens	https://youtu.be/4PkD4JebMAY
The Happy Planet Index	https://www.ted.com/talks/nic_marks_the_happy_planet_index?utm_campaign=tedspread&utm_medium=referral&utm_source=tedcomshare
Seven Principles for Building the Better Cities	https://www.ted.com/talks/peter_calthorpe_7_principles_for_building_better_cities?utm_campaign=tedspread&utm_medium=referral&utm_source=tedcomshare
The Habits of Happiness	https://www.ted.com/talks/matthieu_ricard_on_the_habits_of_happiness?utm_campaign=tedspread&utm_medium=referral&utm_source=tedcomshare

Wiki (Reference purpose only)

Therapeutic Garden	https://en.wikipedia.org/wiki/Therapeutic_garden
Horticultural Therapy	https://en.wikipedia.org/wiki/Horticultural_therapy
Garden Sanctuary	https://en.wikipedia.org/wiki/Garden_sanctuary

Others

Chicago Botanic Garden	https://www.chicagobotanic.org/therapy
Denver Botanic Garden	https://www.botanicgardens.org/beyond/therapeutic-horticulture
Democratic Approach to Therapeutic Gardens	https://dirt.asla.org/2014/06/10/democratic-design/
Interview with Jinny Blom on the Therapeutic Effects on Gardens	https://dirt.asla.org/2012/10/17/interview-with-jinny-blom-on-the-power-of-gardens/

SUSTAINABLE LANDSCAPE DESIGN—WELLNESS GARDEN

Quizzes

© Davidovka/
Shutterstock.com

1. What is the meaning of *Shinrin-yoku*? And, which country is it originated from?

2. What is the name of the soil bacterium that acts to stimulate the production of serotonin?

3. Describe five elements of *feng shui*.